The Nautical Institute

Maritime Security
A practical guide
Second edition

by

Steven Jones MSc BSc (Hons) MNI

Maritime Security
A practical guide
Second edition

by

Steven Jones MSc BSc (Hons) MNI

Steven Jones has asserted his right under the Copyright, Designs and Patents Act 1988 to be identified as the author of this book

Published by The Nautical Institute
202 Lambeth Road, London, SE1 7LQ, UK

Tel: +44 (0)20 7928 1351   Fax: +44 (0)20 7401 2817   Web: www.nautinst.org

Second edition © The Nautical Institute 2012

Book Editor Margaret Freeth
Design and typesetting by PMD Visual Communications
Images courtesy of Danny Cornelissen (www.portpictures.nl), USCG, US Navy
Printed in the UK by Geerings Print Ltd

ISBN 978 1 906915 45 2

Acknowledgements

Numerous people and organisations helped in the production of this book, providing well-placed advice, guidance and expertise. In particular I would like to thank the following, as the book would not have been possible without their efforts, support, and assistance. Thank you:

Stephen Askins, Ince and Co

Dr Phil Anderson FNI, ConsultISM Ltd

Captain Thomas Brown, Seacurus Ltd

Peter Cook, Security Association for the Maritime Industry (SAMI)

Ray Gibbons, Sentinel Maritime Ltd

Bridget Hogan and **Margaret Freeth**, The Nautical Institute

The International Transport Intermediaries Club (ITIC)

Adrian King, Allen Vanguard Ltd

Howard Leedham MBE, STL Maritime Ltd

Gianna Molica-Franco, Seren Creative Ltd

Captain Stuart Nicholls, Stratum Five Ltd

Julian Parker FNI OBE

Anneley Pickles, Shiptalk Ltd

Roy Winfield

Michael Williams, MIRIS International Ltd

Foreword

by **Rear Admiral Sir Efthimios E Mitropoulos** KCMG FNI

Secretary General Emeritus
The International Maritime Organization

Seafarers over the centuries have been aware of the vulnerability of their ships to hostile acts and opportunistic pirates, but the emergence of the political terrorist has now added a new dimension to maritime security.

The maritime industry cannot change the cultural values of societies and should not be expected to do so. However, ships and seafarers are the facilitators of international trade and, as well as being potential targets, they may also be innocent carriers of illegal cargoes under fraudulent manifests, so fuelling the very threats they seek to avoid.

It was for this reason, with the terrorist attacks on the United States in September 2001 acting as a catalyst, that the IMO undertook to coordinate the response to the threat of maritime terrorism both to ships and to the ports they visit.

The maritime industry needed a coordinated, global response. The result was Chapter XI-2 of the SOLAS Convention and the International Ship and Port Facility Security Code, now widely known as the ISPS Code.

While ships are seen as the vehicles of international trade, they become most vulnerable to terrorists when in port and in coastal waters. That is why it is vital to ensure that ports are secure and that coastal States can exercise preventive measures to counter such threats.

Introducing mandatory security requirements within shipping has not been easy for an industry that is intensely competitive. The dedication and commitment of companies and sea staff to gain accreditation and crew training certification within a short time of the introduction of the Code was a remarkable achievement; as have been the tremendous efforts made to secure port facilities across the world.

The general level of security awareness and preparedness in shipping today is at a level where vigilance is increased, security checks prevent overt risks and communications between ships and their companies and companies and governments are tactically efficient.

The effect of all this has been to render it much more difficult to perpetrate opportunistic terrorism. If and when an attack does occur, there are instant and organised responses to limit the consequences and identify those involved.

I am delighted to write the Foreword to this practical guide as it brings together, in a very user-friendly way, some of the best practices that have been developed and found to be effective. In doing so, I want to express my sincere appreciation to all those at sea and ashore who have made and continue to make maritime security work. The book will be of value to all who work in the maritime and related industries for its background information, examples, management and training potential.

As seafarers are in the frontline of maritime security and shoulder the burden of this responsibility, it is up to us working ashore to support them. This book is one such contribution.

Contents

For my family and friends, without whom
every success would seem a failure.

Introduction

Maritime security has evolved since the introduction of the ISPS Code on 1 July 2004. This heralded a significant change in the approach of the international maritime community to security and was a pivotal point in its evolution within the shipping industry.

Shipping has for decades been vulnerable to attack, fraud and criminality. This vulnerability stems from a lack of understanding of the security threats posed to ships and crews, and potentially by them, and a consequent lack of investment in security and the training of personnel.

Development of the current risk management approach to maritime security started in 1985 in the wake of the hijacking of the *Achille Lauro* and was codified after the attacks on the World Trade Center in the USA in September 2001.

These attacks demonstrated how exposed transport systems and their infrastructure could be. They made many consider how vulnerable ships are, and how attractive they could be as targets, which was further highlighted by the 2002 attack on the VLCC *Limburg* off Yemen.

If the aviation sector, which had always been at the vanguard of security innovation and investment, could suffer at the hands of terrorists then shipping was starting to look like a very soft target indeed. The maritime industry had in reality done very little since the end of the Second World War to secure and protect its people, vessels and clients and it became increasingly obvious that a change was needed.

Security advice had long been issued to the maritime industry but it was in the face of an ever increasing onslaught of piracy, terrorism, stowaways and drug smuggling that the shipping industry started to truly harden itself against being a potential target.

The issue of security has also seen changes to the traditional role of the IMO, with the ISPS Code extending its sphere of influence beyond ships and into the shore elements that serve them.

The IMO doesn't intend that its influence should extend into the entire port area, so for the purposes of the ISPS Code a port facility is defined as the location where the ship/port interface takes place (as determined by the contracting government or the designated authority). This can include areas such as anchorages, waiting berths and approaches from seaward, as appropriate.

Shipping has to balance the difficult and complex demands made by people, ships, ports and cargoes. This book aims to provide an overview of the principles underpinning maritime security and guidance on putting those principles into practice, focusing on the construction of, and adherence to, management systems that will ensure compliance with the legislation.

Starting from an assessment of the many threats facing shipping and ports and the problems associated with particular vessel types and cargoes, this book covers the details contained within the ISPS Code, before looking at the implications of the rules and provision of guidance on maritime security and contingency planning.

It should be used in conjunction with the handbooks in The Nautical Institute's maritime security suite, more details from www.nautinst.org This suite is intended to explain the background to the ship security plan (SSP) and ship and company training manuals, and to provide practical advice and guidance that will inform their development.

Steven Jones MSc BSc (Hons) MNI
Port Sunlight, UK
November 2012

Chapter 1
Threats to maritime trade

KEY ADVICE

- Understanding the threats
- Building a picture of how these affect a particular vessel or trade
- Developing an insight into how best to mitigate their effects

The shipping industry is one of the most regulated in the world, with every aspect covered by strict rules and regulations. Over the years these have evolved and developed into an overall concept of managing risk.

Uppermost in these rules has been the ISM Code, an overarching principle of management that brings together all the legislative requirements and ensures that they are applied and that a vessel is supported from ashore.

As a result of ISM, the shipping industry has developed concepts of safety and of managing safety risks, but there was a gap. Whereas there were regulations covering everything from safety, construction and training, through to stowage, working hours and pollution, security was never a mandatory requirement until the introduction of the ISPS Code.

For the purposes of this publication, the concept of security as normally understood must be expanded to "the state of a shipping company/vessel/crew/port, being or feeling secure" or "the safety of a shipping company/vessel/crew/port against such threats as terrorism, piracy and other criminal activities".

Security is an inherently blurred concept but the crucial difference between security and safety is that security has to take into account the actions of active malicious agents attempting to cause destruction.

To use a sporting analogy, safety is akin to mountaineering. If the climber plans properly and is trained and equipped, he will get to the summit. Security is more like football – individuals and the team can be as prepared as possible but the outcome is always in doubt as the other team is actively trying to win.

Most security measures, and particularly those involving ships, entail some degree of compromise. Ships are often placed in dangerous places and situations but to secure a ship 100% would mean that its operational capacities would have to be reduced. A ship without a cargo is effectively redundant, so in order to continue trading some compromises have to be made, meaning there are threats that have to be managed.

Terrorism

It is true to say that the introduction of the ISPS Code and the general formalisation of maritime security were spurred on by the supposed threat of sustained global terrorism, and in particular by the fear and panic that has gripped the world in the wake of various terrorist atrocities. But what is terrorism, and is shipping actually under threat of attack?

For a number of years after the introduction of the ISPS Code the terror threat posed to shipping never really materialised. However documentation reportedly found by US forces upon capturing the al Qaeda leader, Osama bin Laden, indicated that attacks on shipping were being considered by the terrorist organisation.

There have long been problems in producing an accepted and clear definition of terrorism. The United Nations defines it as "any action… that is intended to cause death or serious bodily harm to civilians or non-combatants when the purpose of such an act is to intimidate a population or to compel a government or an international organisation to do or to abstain from doing any act".

The lack of agreement on a definition of terrorism has been a major obstacle to meaningful international countermeasures. Cynics have often commented that one state's 'terrorist' is another's 'freedom fighter'. While it is easy to understand this line of thinking there needs to be a starting point to assess the threat posed to shipping and seafarers. This publication will follow the UN definition while also holding onto the simpler yet all-encompassing concept that "terrorism is violence or a use of force that we disapprove of".

A consistent lesson of crime and terrorism is that the perpetrators increasingly aim at what they perceive as soft targets. The nature of shipping has meant that attacking maritime targets has never been particularly easy, requiring a greater sophistication in planning, training and coordination than those aimed at many land-based facilities or infrastructures. This is why maritime terrorism is relatively rare, and why terrorists have looked at more obvious objectives.

However, as other targets, such as the aviation industry, have tightened security, terrorists are increasingly likely to set their sights wider and contemplate maritime targets.

Using a ship to smuggle goods or weapons, sinking a vessel in a major shipping thoroughfare, using a ship as a weapon, or even attacking maritime vessels, are all definite possibilities and should not be discounted.

The US government has set out a list of what it believes are the likely scenarios for maritime terrorist attack capabilities. In the 2007 Congressional Research Service study *Maritime Security: Potential Terrorist Attacks and Protection Priorities* the scenarios included explosives-laden suicide boats and light aircraft; using merchant and cruise ships as kinetic weapons to ram another vessel, warship, port facility or offshore platform; commercial vessels as launch platforms for missile attacks; swimmers to infiltrate ports; and unmanned underwater explosive delivery vehicles.

It believes that terrorists could also take advantage of a vessel's legitimate cargo, such as chemicals, petroleum or LNG, as the explosive component of an attack. Vessels could be used to transport powerful conventional explosives or weapons of mass destruction (WMD) for detonation in a port or alongside an offshore facility.

The global supply chain is vulnerable to disruption by terrorists. Port facilities are inherently vulnerable because they must provide access by land and sea and because they are sprawling installations, often close to population centres.

Likewise, the ships that transport the products are vulnerable because they travel on direct routes that are known in advance and, for part of their journey, may have to travel through waters that do not allow them to manoeuvre away from possible attacks.

Since so many different players are involved, terrorists have the opportunity to probe the supply chain for the weakest link. While the extent of the threat posed to shipping by terrorists cannot be fully known, the industry needs to adopt a hardened stance and ensure that adequate and effective measures are in place.

Piracy

Full details on piracy, its effects and the means to manage the shipboard response can be found in The Nautical Institute's *Piracy Handbook*.

Piracy is an ancient and established threat to ships, people and cargoes. Over the past 30 years we have found ourselves in the grip of a modern piracy epidemic, with a form of piracy that has evolved into a faster, more ruthless, more organised and violent threat than ever before.

Modern piracy is violent, bloody and ruthless and is made all the more fearsome because its victims know they are alone and defenceless. Seafarers have a basic human right to expect to sail on safe ships in safe waters and no one ashore can fully appreciate the trauma these types of attacks can cause, both physically and mentally.

The motivation behind acts of piracy can vary, depending on where they occur and by whom they are perpetrated. Theft of cash and valuables, particularly from the Master's safe, is often involved but all kinds of ship's stores have been taken, including the contents of upper deck lockers and stores. In some cases entire ships have been stolen, their cargo taken and their crew murdered and the ship subsequently sold.

A record number of ships and crew were hijacked in 2010, most off the coast of Somalia, according to the London-based International Maritime Bureau. Fifty-three vessels with 1,181 crew members were taken, the highest number the IMB has yet seen. Numbers for 2011 to date indicate a continuation of the rising trend.

Of the hijackings, 49 were off the coast of Somalia. In September 2012, 11 vessels and some 188 hostages were still being held by Somali pirates. The numbers fluctuate but with the length of hijackings increasing, costs of release rising and an increasing frequency and ferocity of attacks, there is no sign of the problem diminishing.

It is vital to closely monitor security in areas into which ships trade or transit. The security seascape does shift and it is important to remain aware of the threats posed.

The people problem

Full details on the security implications of stowaways and illicit boarders, the effect on companies and vessels and the means to manage the shipboard response can be found in The Nautical Institute's *Stowaways Handbook*.

The imposition by the ISPS Code of a formal security management system and framework for ships and ports to follow has given a more structured approach to dealing with the problem of stowaways as they are not acceptable from an operational or legislative perspective.

It is generally recognised by all sides of the shipping industry that there is an urgent need for international agreement on the allocation of responsibilities to enable the successful resolution of cases involving stowaways.

The term stowaway refers to any person found on board a ship without authorisation, with intent to travel with the vessel. The initial status of stowaways is usually unclear. They may be refugees attempting to escape war or religious persecution, migrants looking to raise their standard of living, political asylum seekers in search of relief from oppression, illegal immigrants hoping to enter a country undetected or criminals who may be involved with drug trafficking or other illegal activities.

Whatever their motivation, stowaways pose significant security, safety, commercial and liability issues for shipping. The stowaway problem is a serious one and shows no sign of abating. It is part of the much wider problem of migrants at sea.

The factors that compel people to leave their homes are widely recognised and include poor living standards, lack of jobs and opportunities, overpopulation and oppressive regimes, regional conflict, political instability and natural disasters.

They see opportunities in developed industrial nations and believe that life will be better there. Shipping is an attractive mode of transport, given its international nature and relative accessibility.

As well as hardening themselves to minimise the risks of boarding, vessels must have procedures in place for effective searches and a formal response when stowaways are discovered onboard.

Finding stowaways onboard demands a response, from care through to repatriation. It is never straightforward or swift to resolve a stowaway case, so it is important that they are not able to board the vessel in the first place.

Criminal activities

Full details on prevention, detection and managing the shipboard response to criminal activities can be found in The Nautical Institute's *Crime At Sea Handbook*.

Smuggling is a well established security threat to shipping, whether of drugs, contraband or other illegal products and goods.

Control of many smuggled items is often a wider cargo interest's issue, but there is an inherent duty to keep the vessel free of illegal and unwanted items.

The illegal drug trade is a global black market, dedicated to the cultivation, manufacture, distribution and sale of substances that are subject to drug prohibition laws.

In its 2012 report the United Nations Office on Drugs and Crime (UNODC) estimates that globally 230 million people (5% of the world's adult population) used an illicit drug at least once in 2010.

The global illicit opiate and cocaine markets represent two of the biggest transnational drugs and crime threats. The opiate market generates an annual turnover of up to $65 billion, of which some $55 billion is for heroin.

Moreover, the opiate market is interlinked with severe national and international security problems, particularly in Afghanistan and Pakistan. Estimates suggest that the global retail sales figure for cocaine (some $88 billion) is even higher than for opiates.

The role of shipping within the illegal movement of drugs is a concern, and another driver behind efforts to improve security.

The security of cargo shipments is important, so the relationship with the charterer and the Port Facility Security Officer (PFSO) can be important in safeguarding vessels. Where cargo is onboard and there are suspicions of smuggling, a search regime is important.

Starting the security process

The ISPS Code is a starting point, a baseline from which assessment of maritime security vulnerabilities can begin. The same management techniques and philosophies that have begun to make the shipping industry safer can be applied to address those vulnerabilities.

Making shipping secure is not a simple task, but with understanding and investment the guidelines and incentives to make it work are in place.

Chapter 2

Threats to shipping

KEY ADVICE

- Understanding the threats
- Understanding the threats facing specific vessel types
- Understanding the threats facing ports
- Assessing the security significance of known chokepoints
- Understanding the role of design and ergonomics in developing more secure vessels

Different vessels, cargoes and geographical locations all pose different security risks. This chapter will assess the risks to specific vessel types and within certain geographical areas.

A 2008 report from the US Government Accountability Office (GAO) on maritime security considered that three types of attack on vessels or port facilities were the most likely: suicide, standoff and armed assault (GAO-08-141 *Maritime Security: Federal Efforts Needed to Address Challenges in Preventing and Responding to Terrorist Attacks on Energy Commodity Tankers*).

In the maritime domain, suicide attacks have been carried out using a small, explosive-laden boat or a vehicle that the attacker rams into a vessel or energy facility. The intent of such an attack is maximum damage to human or physical targets without concern for the life of the attacker.

Previous attack history underlines terrorist intentions and capability to use small boat attacks. Moreover, intelligence experts say that the suicide boat attack uses a proven, simple strategy that has caused significant loss of life and damage to commercial and military vessels.

Several suicide attacks have been carried out against tankers and energy infrastructure in the Persian Gulf region. They have taken place in restricted waterways where a ship's ability to manoeuvre or engage the attackers is hampered or when a ship has stopped or moored.

In April 2004 terrorists attacked the Al-Basrah and Khawr Al'Amaya offshore oil terminals in Iraq using vessels packed with explosives. Several oil tankers were either docked at, or in the vicinity of, the offshore terminals during the attack. Even though the speedboats detonated prematurely and missed striking the oil tankers and the offshore terminals, another small craft near the Khawr Al'Amaya terminal exploded when coalition forces attempted to intercept it, killing two US Navy sailors and a US Coast Guardsman.

According to the GAO study on maritime terrorism, the coordinated attack appears to have been part of an overall terrorist strategy to destabilise Iraq and both terminals were shut down for two days, resulting in lost revenue of nearly $40 million.

Another suicide attack took place in October 2002 when terrorists rammed the French supertanker *Limburg* as it slowed for a pilot to approach the Ash Shihr Terminal off the coast of Yemen. The resulting explosion breached the Limburg's double-hull and ignited oil stored on board the vessel. An estimated 90,000 barrels of oil were spilled, one crewman was killed and 17 were injured.

In addition to maritime suicide attacks, terrorists have also targeted energy facilities on land. In February 2006, for example, terrorists attempted to drive vehicles packed with explosives through the gates of a major oil processing facility in Saudi Arabia's eastern province. Al Qaeda claimed responsibility for the attack, which killed two Saudi guards and represented the first direct assault on a Saudi oil production facility.

A second type of threat against tankers and attendant maritime infrastructure is a standoff missile attack using a rocket, mortar or rocket-propelled grenade launched from a sufficient distance to evade defensive fire. Standoff missile attacks have been aimed at military ships in ports in the Persian Gulf, but these kinds of attacks also represent a serious threat to tankers. Terrorists launched such an attack using Katyusha rockets in 2005, narrowly missing two US naval ships moored at a Jordanian port. Compared to suicide attacks, standoff attacks are easier to execute but are likely to be less effective, according to intelligence experts. The range, size and accuracy of explosive projectiles used in such an attack could vary considerably.

Armed assaults, particularly at critical shipping chokepoints, represent a third major type of threat to tankers along the energy supply chain, according to the IMB.

These attacks on vessels have taken place where maritime security is lacking and they have been carried out in most cases by pirates seeking to gain control of the ship for financial gain, including petty theft and kidnapping of crew for ransom.

Historically, attacks against tankers and cargo ships have taken place in numerous locations, including off the coast of Somalia, in the Gulf of Guinea, the Persian Gulf and along the Strait of Malacca.

Other types of threat that are considered less likely to occur include crew conspiracies and collisions.

US Coast Guard intelligence reports suggest a hypothetical possibility that crew members (or persons posing as crew members) could conspire to commandeer a vessel with the intent of using the vessel as a weapon or for disrupting maritime commerce.

While many within the shipping industry do not consider this to be a serious threat, it is possible that vessels could be used to transport terrorists or weapons, whether unwittingly or through crew collusion.

One scenario related to armed assaults involves pirates or terrorists deliberately causing a collision by hijacking a large ship and ramming it into a tanker, an energy facility or critical infrastructure such as a bridge.

Although such a scenario requires gaining control of a ship, the successful takeover of aircraft by terrorists in the 11 September 2001 attacks demonstrates that this could be feasible. To date, there have been no known cases of terrorists intentionally using a vessel as a weapon but there have been some close calls in pirate-prone areas.

The most high profile incident occurred in 2003 when pirates gained control of the chemical tanker *Dewi Madrim* in the Strait of Malacca. Once at the tanker's helm, the pirates altered the ship's speed, disabled communications and steered the ship for over an hour before escaping with equipment and technical documents.

Cyber threats

Cyber terrorists pose an increasingly feasible threat. The majority of vessels are extremely high-tech and dependence on satellite communications, electronic control systems and integrated bridge systems is growing. This means that vessels are open to attack from persons hacking into their systems and introducing bugs, viruses and false data.

Cyber attacks are also a low cost and risk-free option for terrorists. While initial consideration of cyber attack has been directed at port infrastructure, there have been reports of merchant ships having incorrect (and unexpected) GPS readings, with suggestions that ship's equipment can be tampered with remotely.

The consequences of spurious data being fed remotely into a vessel's GPS, or of control being taken of a tanker's machinery or pumping equipment, could be extremely serious.

Thankfully there does not appear to be any evidence of serious cyber attacks on vessels, although anecdotal rumours have suggested that the grounding of a German cruise ship was caused by a form of cyber attack on its navigation systems. This has never been confirmed, however. Vigilance and awareness remain important.

There have also been accusations that North Korea has jammed GPS signals and GPS jamming equipment can be bought extremely cheaply on the internet.

Vessels with a significant reliance on electronic control systems and remote position reference systems, such as dynamic positioning vessels, would be especially vulnerable to cyber attack.

Given their work in sensitive areas, and often at close quarters, the potential for externally-induced accidents can be seen as significant.

Officers on all types of ships should be alert to the potential effects of forms of cyber sabotage and the old lessons of being familiar with the situation beyond the wheelhouse can become even more significant if miniscule errors can be input into vessel control systems.

Information technology and communications security should be considered as a standard function onboard today's highly sophisticated vessels. It is vital that shipping companies adequately assess their vulnerability to such cyber and electronic threats and have effective security in place for all systems and equipment.

Threats to specific vessel types

Oil tankers

Tankers make extremely vulnerable targets. They can be extremely large, comparatively slow and cumbersome, are often operated by a small crew, carry a commodity that has great political implications, and have no protection and nowhere to hide.

In moving oil from the wells to the refineries and then to the market place, tankers transport millions of barrels of oil every day. This transportation system has always been a weak link within the oil industry but has become even more vulnerable since the threat of terrorism emerged.

As most of the West's oil is imported, terrorist groups could disrupt the free flow of crude oil into Europe, Japan and the US by damaging or threatening oil transportation routes.

Disruption of oil flows through any of these routes could have a significant impact on oil prices, which are already reaching all-time highs globally. Given that a significant percentage of current oil and gas exploration and production takes place in areas of political risk, including Algeria, Bolivia, the Caspian region, Indonesia, Iran, Iraq, Libya, Nigeria, Russia, Saudi Arabia, Sudan and Venezuela, the potential for disruption or attack is great.

There are many possible forms of attack, ranging from missiles to divers and small boats loaded with explosives. In many instances, even with the provisions of ISPS and the best possible security regime in place, a vessel could still be at risk of damage from such attacks.

If a VLCC were to be attacked, as demonstrated by the *Limburg*, there are a number of likely repercussions. If the attack succeeds and the vessel is destroyed or badly damaged there is potential for:

- Loss of seafarer's lives, or injuries
- Pollution
- Severe disruption to other vessels if sunk in a major shipping lane
- Financial implications for the vessel's hull and machinery, cargo and P&I insurers
- Dramatic increase in insurance premiums for the area of the attack, vessel and cargo
- Publicity for the terrorist group which has attacked the vessel
- Negative publicity for the shipping company and the port area in which the attack occurs
- Loss of revenue for the vessel owner
- Vessels avoiding the area, leading to potential oil shortages in importing nations

It is recognised that tankers transiting well-known oil shipping routes, particularly the Persian Gulf and Horn of Africa, are at a high risk of attack. The threat from terrorists is not limited to shipping lanes but includes ports, loading and off-loading facilities and support infrastructure located inland.

In addition to threats on the high seas, these vessels must pass through narrow straits in hazardous areas such as the entrance to the Red Sea (Bab-el-Mandeb), the Persian Gulf (Strait of Hormuz) and the Strait of Malacca (for further details see p 29).

These are all narrow enough that a single burning VLCC and its spreading oil slick could block the route for other tankers and vessels, with significant consequences for the global oil market. They are also controlled by countries in which terrorists are known to operate. The threat of attack on tankers and their infrastructure was emphasised in a 2002 statement from al Qaeda's Political Bureau which said: "The operation of attacking the French oil tanker [*Limburg*] is not merely an attack against a tanker – it is an attack against international oil transport lines and all its various connotations." This threat was further corroborated by the seizure of terrorist material after the death of Osama bin Laden. Terrorists are seemingly well aware of the strategic value of oil tankers as targets and their susceptibility to attack.

To mitigate the risks of such attacks, the company and the vessel must be fully aware of the threats in areas they are visiting and able to respond quickly to any advice given by contracting governments. In such cases, the ISPS regimes onboard and within the company should foster a rapid response and a better appreciation of mitigating strategies.

Pirates also see tankers as attractive targets. Off Somalia, in the Gulf of Aden and out into the Indian Ocean, pirates believe that tankers taken for ransom can earn higher pay-outs than other vessels – and this seems to be proved by record payments made to free VLCCs in captivity.

According to the UK P&I Club, an extremely worrying new piracy trend is developing off West Africa. Previous attacks off the coast have usually involved petty theft and pilferage while the higher profile, large-scale attacks have been politically motivated.

Recently, however, pirate groups have turned their attentions to the wholesale theft of oil cargoes from tankers. The latest attack profiles have seen gangs board vessels, then destroy all communications equipment and transfer oil from the tanker into their own small tanker vessels.

The operations have been known to take as long as four days and the vessels and crew are effectively hijacked for the duration of the theft.

While the scale of the piracy has increased, so too has the geographic spread. Pirate activity had previously been confined to port areas or the politically sensitive Bonny River and Niger Delta regions, now the pirates are reaching further afield and even into foreign territories to capture vessels.

As tankers have moved further offshore away from the danger zone around Lagos to transfer cargoes, so too have the pirates. They have been known to operate along the coasts of Benin and Cotonou.

The pirates are believed to be Nigerian and the push outwards is believed to be a direct response to the successes of the Nigerian Navy in its own territorial sea.

Gas and chemical tankers

LNG tankers have much in common with their oil-carrying relatives, although they are more conspicuous and offer an even greater potential for destruction. While not all have distinctive storage tanks sitting like humps on the decks, the majority do and their identity is unlikely to be mistaken. Terrorists are not likely to have problems locating one as a target.

The greater part of the world's LNG supply comes from countries with large natural gas reserves, including Algeria, Australia, Brunei, Indonesia, Libya, Malaysia, Nigeria, Oman, Qatar and Trinidad and Tobago.

LNG is cooled at extremely low temperatures (-161°C) and high pressure until it contracts into a clear, colourless, odourless liquid that can be transported worldwide by tankers. The liquid is then unloaded at re-gasification terminals that turn it back into gas fed into pipelines for distribution.

LPG vessels are attractive and high-profile targets and are also unmistakable for any would-be attacker.

The number and range of cargoes carried on product and chemical tankers makes it difficult to do justice to the possible threats and the effects of an attack on such vessels. They make conspicuous targets because of their complex deck arrangements used to contain, load and discharge their cargoes. They are often relatively small and can be found in a large number of smaller ports and seaways.

The one common thread is the fact that their cargoes are highly dangerous. They can be volatile, carcinogenic, flammable, highly toxic, irritant or explosive, or combinations of all these. An attack on such a vessel could have extremely serious and far-reaching consequences.

It is vital therefore that the SSP and all security provisions adequately reflect the cargo and the threat profile of the vessel and trading area.

Container ships

In terms of security, container vessels are unusual as they are generally thought of as being more likely to deliver a terrorist attack than the subject of one.

Despite their size and the value of their cargoes, a direct attack on even the largest container ship would probably not achieve the devastation, financial fallout and environmental damage possible through an attack on an oil or LNG tanker.

Often the largest threat posed to container vessels is from their cargo and in many instances this threat is not aimed at the vessel but at placing the container within the port or country of the terrorist's choice.

Millions of containers arrive in Europe, Japan and the US each year and each could potentially contain explosives, biological agents or WMD. Containers are also a primary means to smuggle people and contraband on ships and through ports. To counter this threat, numerous rules and regulations have been introduced to tighten the security of the entire supply chain.

A range of exercises has demonstrated the theory underpinning the US approach to containers as the concept of 'trusted' shippers that has long been used in the aviation industry is further developed and refined. This is designed to have as little impact as possible on the free and fast movement of goods.

The majority of the world's finished goods move by container and the trade needs to stay at the forefront of rapid cargo transit. Operators within the supply chain are often the first to trial and develop new technology to keep the movement of containers flowing.

The use of radio frequency identification tags (RFID) has been mooted as a possible solution to the opposing demands of fast turnaround and secure cargo. RFID is being used to track containers as they move, with real-time locations both at sea and in ports.

The RFID tag consists of a microchip attached to a radio antenna. The microchip contains information about the type of cargo, manufacturer, serial number, etc. A variety of tags are now available, including passive, active and low, high and ultra-high frequency.

Containers with RFID container seals enable shippers and carriers to:

- Consistently monitor container security and integrity
- Verify that a container was loaded at a secure loading point
- Significantly reduce the likelihood of tampering in transit, with container accountability from point of origin to destination
- Gather enough data to conduct a 'virtual' inspection in advance of arrival
- Guarantee that shipping containers meet governmental security regulations

Satisfying government regulations will ensure containers receive fast track handling through Customs at the point of dispatch and the point of receipt.

Bulk carriers

Bulk carriers carry large quantities of non-packed commodities, the three major being iron ore, coal and grain. Thousands of bulk carriers trade around the world and they are very much the workhorses of the global fleet.

Bulkers come in all sizes but in the main are relatively slow moving, cumbersome and operated by small crews. They are often targeted by pirates. Some of these attacks do escalate into hijacks and subsequent 'phantom' ship cases but in the main bulk carriers are simply the targets of opportunists who see a slow-moving vessel with little sign of life onboard as a relatively easy picking.

As with any large vessel, if one were sunk in a strategic place or used to run into bridges or other vessels, this would cause major problems. In the main, bulk carriers appear to have slipped down terrorists' priorities as they focus on the high profile of tankers and cruise ships or the 'big bang' potential of LNG tankers.

Bulk carrier cargoes are not without their dangers. Ammonium nitrate (fertiliser) is a common cargo and is also highly sought after as an explosive agent. A ship carrying fertiliser could easily become a potent weapon in the wrong hands. There are also occasional cases where intelligence suggests that terrorists may seek to introduce biological agents into dry bulk cargoes, especially foodstuffs such as grains or sugar.

It is often the case that bulk carriers and their cargoes can arouse suspicion and be subjected to enforcement actions as they are loaded in ports outside the strictly controlled wet bulk and container trades.

Passenger vessels and cruise ships

Passenger vessels have long been considered as leaders in maritime security. In the wake of the *Achille Lauro* attack, the cruise industry immediately undertook a concerted reassessment of security vulnerabilities and sought to address them.

For the cruise industry, its highest priority is to ensure the safety and security of passengers and crew. Should a terrorist attack occur, passengers' perception of this and the fear of travelling, including cruising, that might develop could have a hugely detrimental effect on the industry.

Most cruise vessels had almost all the requirements of the ISPS Code included in their security plans years before the July 2004 implementation deadline. Measures in place included designated ship security officers (SSO), company security officers (CSO), approved ship and terminal security plans, as well as the screening of all passengers, crew and items coming onto a ship.

It has long been common to screen all passenger baggage, carry-on luggage, ship stores and cargo and to impose intensified screening of passenger lists and identification.

Passengers and crew pass through metal detectors before boarding and crew and port officials examine every shipment of supplies brought aboard. When ships are in port, watches are posted on deck and at night the decks are lit and ropes secured.

The ships are also keeping records of who is and who is not aboard at any given time and most major companies now have automated systems that enable security personnel to see exactly who is on the ship at any given moment.

These strict security policies and procedures are mirrored at many international cruise terminals, with screening measures similar to those found at airports.

Procedures include the use of metal detectors and photo identification is required for all passengers and crew members at every point of embarkation. All ship personnel and crew must undergo similar luggage and photo identification checks. In addition, ship stores are screened by x-ray, trained dogs or other available and acceptable methods.

Additional security measures include:

- Restriction of onboard access and movements to sensitive vessel areas, such as the bridge and engine room
- Onboard security measures to deter unauthorised entry and illegal activity
- An appropriate security zone around the ship

Cruise ships are very different from the rest of the merchant fleet, with different priorities and patterns of investment. They are free to operate with security as a higher priority than other vessels. Cruise ships are also relatively easy to contain – their design makes it easier to control and limit access. When a ship is in port, passengers and crew can only enter through one or two controlled access points, where ship's security personnel can check IDs and manifests.

Some cruise lines hire former military and naval personnel to implement and oversee their security, while others hire private security firms or former law enforcement officers.

In the past, most security measures were intended to deal with passenger disturbances, as the size of cruise ship populations can see all the social and criminal problems of a small town.

This focus has now shifted and is directed towards maintaining a safe and secure environment and eliminating or mitigating the threat of harm to passengers, crew and ship. Each port call is reviewed and assessed for its history of security-related incidents, stowaway threat, contraband threat, shore-side security operations and equipment and any intelligence that leads the company to believe that the vessel could be under threat.

Cruise ships have been at the forefront of maritime CCTV provision. Much of the initial coverage was focused on casino areas to protect against crime and fraud. Provision has since been rolled out across all parts of vessels, enabling security personnel, officers, staff and crew to visually monitor virtually every area of the ship.

Coverage includes embarkation areas, corridors, public rooms, entry points and common deck areas such as the promenade and pool areas and restricted areas, including crew areas, machinery spaces and navigation and control areas.

Additional legislation has been passed in the US in response to some high profile criminal investigations that indicated there were still gaps in cruise ship security. The Cruise Vessel Security & Safety Act 2010 places a clear emphasis on containing security threats onboard and protecting passengers. It also includes provision for proper and effective investigations when incidents do occur.

In response to a range of particular events, the Act also imposes:

- Balcony guard rails to reach 54 inches in height
- Entry doors of each passenger stateroom and crew cabin to have peep holes, security latches and time-sensitive key technology

- Technology to detect when a passenger falls overboard
- Procedures to determine which crew members have access to staterooms and when

The Act sets out a potential blueprint for cruise vessels to follow. With passenger numbers expected to soon top 20 million annually, there are pressures to ensure that the rule of law is applied effectively at sea and that a transparent approach is taken to reporting deaths, missing individuals, alleged crimes, and passenger and crew member complaints regarding theft, sexual harassment and assault.

Such reporting necessitates improved crime scene response, with training for crew members as appropriate.

Ferries

As a target, ferries have all the attractions of a cruise vessel in that they have a high profile and large numbers of people who would be affected by an attack. Despite this, ferries have never fully adopted the security mentality of cruise ships and so represent relatively soft targets.

Ferries come in all shapes and sizes and serve a multitude of different ports and trades. The largest are indeed targets for terrorists and are extremely susceptible to devices brought onboard by passengers.

Many ferry operators are faced with a problem. Most routes depend on high passenger and cargo volumes and fast turnarounds. Security is often compromised to accommodate commercial concerns.

In the US there has long been concern that ferry services could come under attack, especially in the light of reports that terrorists may have been monitoring and recording details of ferry operations.

Public transport systems all over the world have long been a favourite target of terrorists, and it is no surprise that ferries are now appearing on their target lists.

In Asia, there has been a history of attacks on ferries, particularly in the Philippines. In 2005, Abu Sayyaf was believed to have planted an explosive device on board the ferry *Dona Ramona* as it was about to depart from port. The improvised explosive device (home-made bomb) was wrapped in a pile of clothes atop a number of LPG tanks. The ensuing explosion ripped through the ferry causing serious injury to at least 30 passengers.

In this particular incident it appears that security failed as not only were the terrorists able to get the IED onboard but also, by posing as passengers, to get close to a restricted area (LPG storage point).

Cable ships, survey and specialist vessels

Generally speaking, vessels engaged in specialist operations, such as cable laying and repair, seismic surveying, dredging and navigation mark maintenance, do not have a particularly high threat profile.

In reality, however, they could become attractive targets to opportunistic maritime crime as they tend to do 'strange things, in strange places'. Often such vessels work close to land and move extremely slowly, if moving at all, in places of unrest and of high criminal activity.

On the positive side, when these vessels are operating they often display a high level of activity on deck, with movement of personnel and lighting. All involved with such vessels must remain acutely aware of the target they may become when working in potentially threatening areas.

The CSO should make decisions in dialogue with the vessel's flag state to explore the idea of operating at raised security levels when working close to land.

Offshore vessels

For the offshore sector, there is the added issue that vessels can become targets owing to the politically sensitive nature of their employment.

The targeting of offshore vessels and crews working in the Niger Delta, for instance, is related to the continuing dispute between the Movement for the Emancipation of the Niger Delta (MEND) and the Nigerian government.

The exploitation of oil and the conflict this has caused have put these vessels at risk and it is vital that company and shipboard security regimes reflect this.

In addition there are environmental concerns. In the past, the security of such ships has been breached by a number of protest groups.

It is also important to recognise the true scale of the threat posed if security is breached. With such vessels working in close proximity to other vessels and hydrocarbon facilities, there is a heightened threat if a vessel were to be used as a kinetic weapon.

Small vessels

There are millions of small vessels (under 500gt) that sail outside the remit of the ISPS Code. Many politicians and people within the shipping industry are slowly waking up to this fact and this could eventually lead to the introduction of new security guidelines to encompass the global fleet of small vessels.

In the light of the importance of small vessel security, the European Commission's Directorate-General for Mobility and Transport has embarked on a study of the impact (including the financial consequences) of extending security measures to ships which currently do not fall within the scope of SOLAS Chapter XI/2 and the ISPS Code.

The EU SeacureSeas project echoes past processes introduced in the US, where the US Department of Homeland Security was prompted to act after recognising that maritime security efforts were focused primarily on large commercial vessels, cargoes and crew. Efforts to address the small vessel environment have largely been limited to traditional safety and basic law enforcement concerns but it was recognised that small vessels are readily vulnerable to potential exploitation by terrorists, smugglers of weapons of WMDs, narcotics, aliens, other contraband and criminals. Small vessels have also been successfully employed overseas by terrorists to deliver waterborne improvised explosive devices (WBIEDs).

While producing the US strategy the federal government readily admitted having "incomplete knowledge of the international recreational boating public, their travel patterns and the facilities they use". This was coupled with limited information available regarding fishing fleets and the multitude of small commercial vessels operating in or near US waters. The issue is extremely complex and potentially contentious but it is not unique to the US. Many of the threats facing the borders, shipping, boats and waters of other nations are similar.

The US authorities deemed that there was a clear need to close security gaps and enhance the small vessel security environment. The Small Vessel Security Strategy (SVSS) provides a coherent framework to improve maritime security and safety through the coordinated efforts of government, law enforcement and local authorities together with international partners, private industry and recreational users of the waterways. It is likely that other nations will follow this lead.

One solution could be to persuade more port authorities to clamp down on unregulated craft by insisting they install low-cost transponders in systems backed by aerial satellites. This approach is being imposed by Singapore.

Within the port of Singapore, authorities have restricted the circulation of small craft and ferries and designated special routes for them. A VTS watchkeeper is designated solely to monitor and communicate with sensitive vessels and there are new guidelines for incoming small vessels to conduct self-assessments, with periodic inspections.

The use of the word 'small' does not really do justice to such vessels. These can be significant craft and it is a definite security challenge to deal with the proportion of mainstream shipping that is not covered by international security legislation.

It should be remembered that ISPS-compliant vessels are obliged to interact with a multitude of these smaller vessels. Given that bunker barges, water barges, pilot launches and tugs will often fall in this category, it is impossible to fully guard against the potential security contamination that could stem from such interactions.

Leisure craft

Leisure craft can also pose a threat. While it is difficult to gain exact figures on the manufacture and sale of such craft, it is understood that an estimated 300,000-500,000 aluminium and fibreglass boats of 14 feet and over are produced each year.

This is a significant number that can only hint at the problems of trying to adequately monitor and police such a global fleet. This estimate ignores the numbers of boats under 14ft and craft such as jet-skis, all of which can pose a threat to shipping if used to deploy explosives.

A small craft packed with explosives was used to great effect in the attacks on the USS *Cole* and the *Limburg*. Clearly these small craft are a security headache and one that the ISPS Code does not address.

Ports as targets

The ISPS Code recognises that security at the ship/port interface is crucial to protecting both ship and port and depends on both parties understanding their responsibilities and working together. For terrorists, ports are extremely attractive targets, especially for those who are intent on damage to trade rather than property or life. For those intent on stowing away or carrying out criminal activities, ports are the way onto the ship they need.

Historically, security at most ports was geared up to keep goods in rather than to keep anything out. In many instances, the perceived threat of terror attacks has led to a complete rethink of security provisions.

Ports are vulnerable to attack from sea and land and have difficulty marrying the demands of commerce (quick throughput of vessels and cargo) with the need to check who and what comes into the port.

Port security is an expensive undertaking and many countries were slow to fully implement their ISPS regimes. It was only when the true commercial realities of non-compliance were realised that the investments of time, money and resources were fully applied.

Security is obviously different for each specific port but in essence contains many of the same elements of physical security, surveillance, waterside access control and patrols.

The need for physical port security has been recognised for many centuries and huge stone walls often characterise the perimeters of old port areas. ISPS requirements have seen many ports invest in effective perimeter security, involving fencing, guard-posts, access control, intruder detection systems (IDS) and guards and patrols.

CCTV systems allow port security personnel to keep a permanent visual cover of all sensitive areas. These systems do not come cheap, particularly if advanced levels of sophistication, data capture and image quality are required.

A port security regime also needs to be able to assess the security implications of cargoes and shipments inside, or arriving at, the port. This involves investment in x-ray technology and scanners to pick up security breaches such as people, drugs, explosives, radiation and illegal shipments.

Ports are naturally vulnerable from sea-borne access, so many security programmes have involved the establishment of port water patrols. Some ports have invested in barriers to effectively close off parts of the port to small craft.

Patrolling is also likely to be increased on the landside part of the port. This will usually consist of a number of guards patrolling to set checkpoints.

Under ISPS, ports have a PFSO whose task is to ensure that the code is followed and that vessels calling into the port have a point of contact regarding security.

Many ports will, if deemed necessary, provide externally supplied guards for a vessel. Each vessel will have to assess its own requirements and any legislative demands made by the port before sanctioning their use. It should be noted that the forced provision of such guards can have significant financial implications.

Where external guards are used, the Ship Security Officer (SSO) should attempt to obtain some form of confirmation from the PFSO of the exact task to be performed by the guards. In the event of an incident, this dialogue may be important for establishing liability.

It must be remembered that each port will have a different level of security capability, from major ports that have invested enormous sums to those in countries and areas where such financial outlay is not possible.

The Company Security Officer (CSO) and SSO should be in contact with the PFSO and should base any security decisions on feedback from this contact and any intelligence they may receive prior to the port call.

It is vital that each vessel does all it can to fully secure itself and should not rely on port security to keep it safe from attack, stowaways or smugglers.

Civil disorder and unrest

All too often vessels are either heading to, or are already alongside, when serious civil unrest breaks out.

It is important that security plans have instructions on potential responses and CSOs should be liaising with the vessel command team on a continuous basis. They should also ensure they are able to access and follow the advice and guidance laid down by contracting governments, whether through the vessel's flag, nationality of the crew or ownership of the vessel or cargo.

It is usual in the face of violent unrest, protest or civil war for organisations such as the US Coast Guard to issue Port Security Advisories. These will suggest security measures for ships when calling at affected ports. Uppermost in these concerns are whether the port facility requirements of the ISPS Code are still being executed and maintained by the port. Depending on the severity of the incident, it may be extremely difficult to determine that effective anti-terrorism measures are in place.

The most common advice is for vessels to:

- Minimise activities in port including crew changes, bunkering and taking on stores
- Take measures consistent with the SSP equivalent to Security Level 2
- Ensure that the vessel and personnel are ready to move to an elevated security level as and when necessary

- Ensure that each access point to the ship is guarded and that the guards have total visibility of the exterior (both landside and waterside) of the vessel
- Attempt to execute a Declaration of Security (DoS)
- Document specific actions taken in the ship's security records as required by Part A, Section 10 of the ISPS Code
- Directly report the actions taken to the CSO and to the appropriate authorities both in the short term and when arriving at the next port.

Seaways, canals and choke points

Cargoes transported by sea generally follow a fixed set of maritime routes. Along these routes, vessels encounter several geographic chokepoints (narrow channels).

These chokepoints are critically important to world oil trade because so much oil passes through them, yet they are narrow and theoretically could be blocked – at least temporarily. Their narrowness makes them susceptible to pirate attacks and shipping accidents. They also bring vessels closer into land and threats could emerge as a result of their visibility.

The major chokepoints are:

Bab el-Mandab

Location: Djibouti/Eritrea/Yemen; connects the Red Sea with the Gulf of Aden and the Arabian Sea.

Closure of the Bab el-Mandab could keep tankers from the Persian Gulf from reaching the Suez Canal, diverting them around the southern tip of Africa (Cape of Good Hope). This would add greatly to transit time and cost and effectively tie up spare tanker capacity.

In addition, closure of the Bab el-Mandab would effectively block non-oil shipping from using the Suez Canal, with significant implications for global trade.

Security remains a major concern in the region, particularly after the *Limburg* attack off the coast of Yemen, plus the proximity to Somalia.

The seasonal effects of the monsoon climate in the Indian Ocean mean that pirates often seek targets in the vicinity of the Bab-el-Mandab so as to avoid the rougher seas in their more traditional area of operation.

Bosphorus/Turkish Straits

Location: Turkey; 17-mile long waterway that divides Asia from Europe and connects the Black Sea with the Mediterranean.

Only half-a-mile wide at its narrowest point, this is one of the world's busiest and most treacherous waterways (50,000 vessel movements annually, including 5,500 oil tankers).

Many of the proposed export routes for forthcoming production from the Caspian Sea region pass westwards through the Black Sea and the Turkish Straits en route to the Mediterranean and world markets. The ports of the Black Sea were the primary oil export routes of the former Soviet Union and the Black Sea remains the largest outlet for Russian oil exports.

Under the Montreux Convention of 1936, commercial shipping has the right of free passage through the Bosphorus and Turkish Straits in peacetime, although Turkey claims the right to impose regulations for safety and environmental purposes.

An attack here could effectively seal the straits for some time, trapping a large number of vessels in the Black Sea.

Panama Canal

Location: Extends approximately 50 miles from Panama City to Colon, connecting the Pacific Ocean with the Caribbean Sea and Atlantic Ocean.

Much of the canal's capacity is taken up by goods moving to and from the US, with the majority of canal traffic moving between the east coast of the US and Asia. Movements between Europe and the west coast of the US and Canada form the second largest trade route at the waterway.

Grain cargoes are the largest commodity (by tonnage) shipped through the canal, followed by petroleum and petroleum products.

The sinking of a vessel in the narrowest parts of the Panama Canal could have a crippling effect on the trade that passes through it.

Strait of Hormuz

Location: Oman/Iran; connects the Persian Gulf with the Gulf of Oman and the Arabian Sea and out to the Indian Ocean.

By far the world's most important oil chokepoint, it consists of 2-mile wide channels for inbound and outbound tanker traffic, as well as a 2-mile wide buffer zone. Closure of the Strait of Hormuz would effectively close the Persian Gulf and the only alternative would be to abandon the use of shipping for oil exports until it could re-open.

The only feasible alternative would be to utilise pipeline routes, including the 5M bpd capacity Petroline (East-West pipeline) and the 290,000 bpd Abqaiq-Yanbu pipeline across Saudi Arabia to the Red Sea.

Strait of Malacca

Location: Malaysia/Singapore; connects the Indian Ocean with the South China Sea and the Pacific Ocean.

The Strait of Malacca is the shortest sea route between three of the world's most populous countries – India, China, and Indonesia – and is considered to be the key chokepoint in Asia.

The narrowest point of this shipping lane is the Phillips Channel in the Singapore Strait, which is only 1.5 miles wide at its narrowest point. This creates a natural bottleneck, with the potential for a collision, grounding or oil spill. If the strait were closed, nearly half of the world's fleet would be required to sail further, generating a substantial increase in the requirement for vessel capacity.

All excess capacity in the world fleet might be absorbed, with the strongest effect on crude oil shipments and dry bulk, such as coal. Closure of the Strait of Malacca would immediately raise freight rates worldwide.

More than 50,000 vessels transit the Strait of Malacca annually. With Chinese oil imports from the Middle East increasing steadily and Chinese demand for steel reaching incredible highs, the Strait of Malacca is likely to grow in strategic importance in the coming years.

It is also a piracy hot spot and the risk of attack is high.

Suez Canal

Location: Egypt; connects the Red Sea and Gulf of Suez with the Mediterranean.

Closure of the Suez Canal would divert tankers around the southern tip of Africa (Cape of Good Hope), adding greatly to transit time and effectively tying up tanker capacity.

The main channels of the canal are dredged to a depth of about 20 metres and the navigational width between buoys is set at 180m. Double channels, where ships travelling in opposite directions can pass without stopping, have been constructed at four locations and cover approximately 41 miles.

The largest ships allowed to pass through the canal may have a beam of up to 64 metres and a draught up to 16 metres.

Projects are continuing to widen and deepen the canal, allowing larger vessels to pass through but also adding to the threat of attack and the consequences when it occurs.

Given the politically sensitive nature of the region, the threat profile is high.

Strait of Gibraltar

Location: Mouth of the Mediterranean, between Spain and Morocco, Gibraltar and Ceuta (Spanish enclave in North Africa).

The Strait of Gibraltar is at an extremely strategic location. Ships that travel from the Atlantic to the Mediterranean, and vice versa, pass through it and there are a number of large ferries which cross between Europe and Africa here.

The depth is about 300m and the strait is approximately 8.5 miles wide at its narrowest point.

The Strait of Gibraltar is a main route for drugs and migrants and there have been terrorist plots singling out the area for attention.

Dover Strait

Location: UK and France; connects the North Sea to the English Channel and onwards to the Atlantic Ocean.

At 21 miles wide at its narrowest point between Dover, UK, and Calais, France, the Dover Strait is a fairly expansive chokepoint. On account of its importance as a shipping highway and the amount of traffic it carries, however, any incident could cause havoc.

This was demonstrated by the sinking of the car carrier *Tricolor* in 2002. The wreck was hit twice more in the ensuing months, until it was finally cut up and cleared.

In addition to these primary chokepoints for global shipping traffic, all ports and rivers have their particular chokepoints and sensitive areas in which attacks and sunken vessels could cripple trade and the free movement of vessels and cargo.

Design of secure ships

There is an obvious difficulty in designing and constructing vessels that are easy to escape from in the event of an accident but which also deter and restrict access to boarders.

When designing and constructing a naval vessel, there are five fundamentals that are always considered, namely speed, seakeeping, strength, style and stability. The ability of merchant vessels to 'trade hurt', in the same way that naval vessels are capable of 'fighting hurt', may become an evolutionary trend in commercial shipping. It would be especially useful for ships to withstand the onslaught of missile-toting pirates.

Increased survivability comes with increased costs. It may be that many companies, after assessing the threats, are willing to simply continue with the traditional approach of transferring the risks through H&M insurance rather than going to the added expense of creating ships that can survive a terrorist attack.

When considering the design and construction of a vessel from a security perspective, the areas of primary concern are:

- Accommodation: reduced access points, but remaining easy to exit
- Protection of vital equipment
- Access control
- Means of access and through routes
- Monitoring of the vessel
- Hull strength
- Emergency exits: the conflict between safety and security should see the development of one universally accepted design

Whatever the changes that may be considered to the design or construction of merchant vessels it should be remembered that apart from losses resulting from biological, chemical, radiological and nuclear attacks, once a security breach has occurred and a vessel has suffered damage the responses and the survivability of the vessel will be the same as in any other emergency.

These are the same fire-fighting, damage limitation and evacuation reactions that should be contained in the vessel's safety management system (SMS).

The most simple and cost-effective changes that can be introduced to allow merchant vessels to comply more easily with ISPS with small crew complements are changes in the ergonomics and layout of vessels.

The layout of access points and means of allowing crew to move around vessels have changed very little over the past half century. For all the changes internally, the ladders, alleyways and railings that form part of the accommodation of today's vessels would be very familiar to mariners of past generations.

It would seem that there is a time for a change and the latest generations of naval vessels may provide inspiration. The most modern destroyers have accommodation and command areas that extend outwards level with the hull. This makes it far easier to control access.

By doing the same for commercial vessels it could make it easier and safer to monitor, manage and respond to security breaches across a larger area.

It is difficult to see who will take the lead in implementing this change towards ergonomic design, however. Despite their increasing involvement in naval vessels, the classification societies are not thought likely to set new design standards for vessels based on ISPS. It is also unlikely that IMO will force any design changes with regards to security, as it simply adopts the standards with which designers need to comply.

This leaves the shipping industry in something of a quandary. The ISPS Code is difficult to apply across today's traditionally designed vessels. The vast majority of the world fleet is built with safety and commerce as its basic functions. The industry therefore needs some radical re-thinking and the development of simple and cost-effective solutions that owners can accept and that will assist personnel to improve the security of their vessels.

The traditional approach of low freeboard, open railings, outside accommodation staircases and open decks is a boon to those posing a threat and makes it very difficult to lock vessels down. It seems a rethink is needed to ensure that vessels are built that are able to combine the demands of business, comfort, safety, environmental concerns and security.

Looking at vessels that have been readied for transit of piracy High Risk Areas, a significant amount of razor wire is required to safeguard access to the vessel and, once onboard, around it. This strongly suggests that security has not been a consideration in the design stage.

Citadels

The use of safe places of refuge, or citadels, onboard vessels at risk of attack by pirates has been on the increase since late 2009. There have been instances where crews have foiled pirates because they could not gain access to the vessel or individual crew members.

However, the benefits of having a locked-down place of refuge are lost if it is not possible to get all personnel inside. It is important to fully understand both the technical aspects of creating a citadel and the operational implications of managing their effective use.

There is a considerable degree of misunderstanding of the citadel concept in merchant shipping. The fact that it is a new concept on commercial vessels, and indeed far removed from usual considerations, has given rise to some difficulties. The industry guidelines (*Best Management Practices to deter piracy off the coast of Somalia and in the Arabian Sea area*) stress that citadels should only be created onboard under the guidance of maritime security experts.

Once constructed, there are other considerations such as preparing and mustering for entry. There are a number of important aspects of making the citadel work. On some vessels, they can be an excellent security solution and work well as part of a layered defence. However, this depends partly on a genuine and functioning security culture within the company and onboard the vessel.

Those who rely on having somewhere where they think they can hide and which they believe will keep them protected, probably need to look at the intricate requirements for making a citadel approach really work.

Reports are emerging that in addition to their usual piracy paraphernalia, pirates are taking plastic explosives onboard with the aim of blasting their way into citadels and strongholds.

Use of, and perhaps overreliance on, citadels has prompted regular updates to advice. It is strongly recommended that citadels are seen as complementary to, rather than a replacement for, all other self-protection measures. NATO has been quick to stress that it remains the responsibility of owners, operators and Masters to decide and implement policy in relation to the use of citadels. It also stresses that the use of a citadel does not guarantee a military response.

The latest industry thinking will be available in the most recent edition of the Best Management Practices (BMP).

Are ships the threat?

Ships by their very nature get everywhere from the smallest town-side ports to the mega-ports, such as Rotterdam, Hong Kong, Long Island and Singapore.

While those within the industry see the threat of terror as pointed at vessels, there are many that see ships as the potential delivery method of a terror strike. It must be remembered that much of this security legislation has evolved to protect ports and states from ships, not to protect ships.

The shipping industry is a complex business that many security forces and governments do not fully understand. Although the industry has modernised, it still maintains many historical business practices. What may seem perfectly normal to a Master, shipbroker or chartering manager may set alarm bells ringing in many law enforcement agencies.

Much has been made of this lack of understanding and measures have been put in place by many authorities to gain better maritime domain awareness.

Many issues come into play – the nature of shipping and its flags of convenience, coupled with the complex way in which shippers, cargo owners, shipowners and crews interact. There appear to be many potential hiding places for those intent on nefarious acts.

The corporate veils shipping has created to confuse issues of ownership and financial liability could be a boon to stateless terrorists because they are capable of hiding not just the bankrupt owner wishing to avoid creditors, but the terrorist, drug smuggler or gun-runner wishing to conceal his tracks.

As vessels shift register, change classification society, switch names and bring new crews from an ever more eclectic range of nations, it must be recognised that these traditional patterns of marine commerce could give the appearance to outsiders that shipping is a terrorist attack waiting to happen.

Ships move relatively freely around the globe and many of them are unhindered by even strict flag state rules. They carry dangerous goods, with fertiliser circling the globe by the kiloton.

While these doubts remain, and many within the shipping industry wish to hide their true identities, vessels will continue to be seen as possible transport for bombs, arms or terrorists and capable of being used to block ports and bring trade to a halt through global sea lanes.

It is an important part of any security regime to recognise the perceptions of threat that the shipping industry poses to others.

Chapter 3

Evolution of maritime security

KEY ADVICE

- Understanding the development of security legislation
- Understanding historical drivers and responses
- Understanding the relationship between IMO, US and European legislation
- Understanding which organisations have a maritime security role

The ISPS Code was adopted by a diplomatic conference held 9-13 December 2002 through amendments to SOLAS Chapters V and XI, which was divided into chapters XI-1 and XI-2. Under the new chapter XI-2, which provides the umbrella regulations, the code became mandatory on 1 July 2004. The tacit acceptance procedure within SOLAS ensured that the code was developed and implemented in a very short period of time.

In February 1984, 20 years before the ISPS Code came into force, the IMO had adopted resolution A.545(13) Measures to prevent acts of piracy and armed robbery against ships. In January 1986, following the hijack of the cruise ship *Achille Lauro*, it adopted resolution A.584 (14) Measures to prevent unlawful acts that threaten the safety of ships and the security of their passengers and crews.

This resolution invited the IMO's Maritime Safety Committee (MSC) to develop detailed and practical technical measures to ensure the security of passengers and crews on board ships, taking into account the work of the International Civil Aviation Organization (ICAO) in the development of standards and recommended practices for airport and aircraft security.

In December 1985, the UN General Assembly called upon the IMO "to study the problem of terrorism aboard or against ships with a view to making recommendations on appropriate measures".

In September 1986, the MSC approved MSC/Circ.443 Measures to prevent unlawful acts against passengers and crew on board ships, which was to apply to passenger ships engaged on international voyages of 24 hours or more and the port facilities serving them.

This was very much the precursor to the ISPS Code. It stated that governments, port authorities, administrations, shipowners and operators, Masters and crews should take appropriate measures to prevent unlawful acts that may threaten passengers and crews. Port facilities and individual ships should have a security plan and appoint a security officer. The conduct of security surveys and the security measures and procedures that should be adopted were described in detail, and security training was also covered.

In 1988, IMO introduced the Convention for the Suppression of Unlawful Acts against the Safety of Maritime Navigation (SUA), which obliged contracting governments to extradite or prosecute those engaged in the perpetration of unlawful acts at sea.

In July 1996, the MSC approved MSC/Circ.754 Passenger ferry security, which was to apply to passenger ferries operating on international routes and the ports serving those routes. The measures could also "be applied to international freight ferry operations depending on the requirements of individual member governments".

All remained relatively dormant on the security front until the adoption in November 2001 of Assembly resolution A.924 (22) Review of measures and procedures to prevent acts of terrorism which threaten the security of passengers and crews and the safety of ships, which led to the adoption of the ISPS Code and amendments to SOLAS in December 2002.

Amendments to SOLAS

SOLAS is an exceptional and powerful tool in the IMO's legislative armoury. It is amended every four years and is very much a living document and the lifeblood of maritime legislation. The tacit acceptance procedure allows SOLAS to stay valid and contemporary. Under this, amendments enter into force on a specific date unless a certain specified number of states object.

The key amendments covered:

Chapter V (Safety of navigation)
Regulation 19: Navigational systems and equipment

Timetable for fitting AIS

Chapter XI (Special measures to enhance maritime safety)
Re-numbered as Chapter XI-1

Chapter XI-1
Regulation 3: Ship identification number

Regulation 5: Continuous synopsis record

Chapter XI-2
Regulation 1: Definitions

Regulation 2: Application

Regulation 3: Obligations of contracting governments

Regulation 4: Requirements for companies and ships

Regulation 5: Specific responsibilities of companies

Minimum information to be supplied to the Master regarding the employment, crewing and operations of the vessel.

Regulation 6: Ship security alert systems

Regulation 7: Threats to ships

Setting of security levels by contracting governments and provision of information to ships

Regulation 8: Master's discretion for safety and security

Regulation 9: Control and compliance measures

Additional regulations include: Regulation 10 Requirements for port facilities; Regulation 11 Alternative security agreements; Regulation 12 Equivalent security arrangements; and Regulation 13 Communication of information

Development of the SUA Convention

Resolution A.924 (22) also led to amendments to the SUA Convention. In the original convention of 1998, unlawful acts included seizure of ships by force, acts of violence against persons on board ships, and the placing of devices on board a ship which are likely to destroy or damage it. By protocols adopted in 2005 that entered into force in July 2010, the list of offences in Article 3 of the convention was expanded to cover a wide range of terrorist acts, including illegal transportation and usage of explosive, radioactive, biological, chemical or nuclear weapons or intimidation of such usage.

It was recognised that as unlawful acts against vessels become more frequent and sophisticated the convention must be able to evolve and remain a valid weapon against terrorists, pirates and criminals.

The amended convention complements the ISPS Code by providing a legal basis for the arrest, detention and extradition of terrorists in the event of a terrorist attack against shipping.

US legislation

The US was the primary force in pushing through the amendments to SOLAS and the ISPS Code and its government provided the IMO with funding for many of the meetings held to debate security during 2002.

The US has also introduced some unilateral maritime security measures, of which the most important is the Maritime and Transportation Security Act (MTSA) of 2002. This was fully implemented on 1 July 2004. While it shares many commonalities with the ISPS Code it goes much deeper into specific requirements for securing US maritime infrastructure and includes sanctions against those who fail to correctly implement the Act.

The MTSA regulations require security officers and training for all personnel, security assessments and plans, alternative security programmes (approved by the US Coast Guard), maritime security directives (issued by USCG), three security levels and Customs, trade and security provisions.

Maritime Security

The Department of Homeland Security views maritime security as three separate and distinct strands: overseas, in transit and in US ports and waters. Each of these stages in the maritime supply chain has its own legislation.

Under the Automated Manifest System (AMS) regulations, all vessels loading or carrying cargoes destined for, or passing through, US ports have to transmit manifest data electronically prior to vessel arrival. This allows Customs and Border Protection (CBP) to screen cargo data through an automated targeting system. Shipments are checked against information stored in law enforcement and commercial databases to identify potentially high-risk shipments before they arrive at US ports.

The AMS regulations also require one of the contract parties to assume the role of 'carrier' for the purpose of submitting cargo information.

CBP offers preferential treatment, including reduced frequency of government security screenings, to importers who participate in the Customs-Trade Partnership Against Terrorism (C-TPAT) programme. Parties throughout the supply chain (including ocean carriers and port authorities and terminal operators) voluntarily agree to perform security self-assessments and adopt C-TPAT recommended guidelines.

The USCG works with other countries to jointly evaluate compliance with the ISPS Code under the International Port Security Program. Information gained by the USCG from visits to these countries is used to improve US security practices and to determine if additional security precautions will be required for vessels arriving from those counties.

CBP also negotiates cargo security agreements with governments of US trading partners under the Container Security Initiative (CSI). This programme establishes procedures for screening and inspecting maritime cargo containers before they are loaded aboard vessels bound for the US.

CSI is currently operational in 58 ports.	
Americas and Caribbean	
Montreal, Vancouver and Halifax	Canada
Santos	Brazil
Buenos Aires	Argentina
Puerto Cortes	Honduras
Caucedo	Dominican Republic
Kingston	Jamaica
Freeport	Bahamas
Balboa, Colón and Manzanillo	Panama
Cartagena	Colombia

Europe	
Rotterdam	Netherlands
Bremerhaven and Hamburg	Germany
Antwerp and Zeebrugge	Belgium
Le Havre and Marseilles	France
Gothenburg	Sweden
La Spezia, Genoa, Naples, Gioia Tauro and Livorno	Italy
Felixstowe, Liverpool, Thamesport, Tilbury, and Southampton	UK
Piraeus	Greece
Algeciras, Barcelona and Valencia	Spain
Lisbon	Portugal
Asia and the East	
Singapore	
Yokohama, Tokyo, Nagoya and Kobe	Japan
Hong Kong	
Busan	South Korea
Port Klang and Tanjung Pelepas	Malaysia
Laem Chabang	Thailand
Dubai	UAE
Shenzhen and Shanghai	China
Kaohsiung and Chi-Lung	Taiwan
Colombo	Sri Lanka
Salalah	Oman
Qasim	Pakistan
Ashdod and Haifa	Israel
Africa	
Durban	South Africa
Alexandria	Egypt

The US has also taken the lead in the Proliferation Security Initiative (PSI), a global response to the perceived threat of WMD, their delivery systems and related materials. Many major trading nations, including Australia, France, Germany, Italy, Japan, the Netherlands, Poland, Portugal, Russia, Spain and the UK, are involved, with 90 other countries cooperating on an informal basis.

PSI participants abide by a Statement of Interdiction Principles, thereby allowing ships suspected of carrying such goods to and from countries of "proliferation concern" to be detained and searched as soon as they enter member countries' territorial waters.

European Union legislation

Member states of the European Union enacted the ISPS Code and amendments to SOLAS through Regulation (EC) No 725/2004 of the European Parliament and Council of 31 March 2004.

This makes mandatory much of the guidance given in Part B of the ISPS Code. It also requires each member state to draw up a list of port facilities on which security assessments have been carried out and the extent of the measures taken to enhance maritime security, and establishes quotas for security checks on ships that exceed those for port state safety inspections. Advance notification of intention to enter an EU port is also imposed, similar to that required in the US.

Every ship intending to enter port is required to provide, in advance, information concerning its International Ship Security Certificate (ISSC) and the levels of security at which it operates and has previously operated.

In October 2005, the European Parliament and Council issued Directive 2005/65/EC to enhance security by covering the entire port, rather than just the ship/port interface as in the ISPS Code. Ports are required to carry out a security assessment, establish a port security plan, nominate a port security officer, identify a supervisory security authority and establish different security levels.

The directive aims at establishing an EU-wide framework for port security that complements the ISPS Code.

Application by member states of EU maritime security legislation is monitored by Commission inspections. These verify the effectiveness of national quality control systems and maritime security measures, procedures and structures at the national level and at individual port facilities and relevant companies.

The European Maritime Safety Agency (EMSA) participates in these inspections and provides the Commission with technical assistance in the performance of the inspection tasks in respect of ships, relevant companies and Recognised Security Organizations (RSOs).

Further developments

Maritime security legislation will evolve to reflect real and perceived risks.

Concerns about inconsistencies between the mandatory Part A of the ISPS Code and the optional Part B were addressed at MSC 87 (May 2010). It was agreed the inconsistencies were not of a nature and scale that required further action and the final decision of the committee was not to amend the code.

Organisations with a maritime security role

Baltic and International Maritime Council

BIMCO is an independent international shipping association with a membership composed of shipowners, managers, brokers, agents and other stakeholders with vested interests in the shipping industry.

The association acts on behalf of its global membership and this has naturally extended to maritime security.

While BIMCO involves itself in the debate on practical security matters, much of its work is on the documentary and facilitation side. Charterparty clauses relating to security are often generated by BIMCO.

Intertanko

Intertanko is an association of independent tanker owners and operators of oil and chemical tankers.

The organisation has 250 members, with a combined fleet of some 3,050 tankers totalling 260 million dwt. It provides a forum for the industry to meet to discuss policies and create statements.

It is a valuable source of first-hand information, opinions and guidance and has been vociferous in its condemnation of violence against seafarers and vessels. The organisation has spearheaded campaigns such as Save Our Seafarers.

International Association of Airport and Seaport Police

IAASP is an international law enforcement and public safety member organisation established in 1968 by police departments having jurisdictional authority over airports and seaports from Canada, the Netherlands and the US.

The organisation works with governments and international organisations such as the United Nations to ensure cooperation and interaction on policy, best practices and operational issues.

International Association of Classification Societies

IACS contributes to maritime safety, security and regulation through technical support, compliance verification and research and development.

More than 90% of the world's cargo-carrying tonnage is covered by the classification design, construction and through-life compliance rules and standards set by its 13 member societies.

The SSPs of the vast majority of ships will have been verified by a classification society which is a member of IACS in the role of RSO for many flag states.

International Chamber of Shipping

ICS is the principal international trade association for merchant ship operators, representing all sectors and trades and about 80% of the world merchant fleet.

It has long been at the forefront of developing maritime security best practice, and the lessons and experiences of ICS members have been made known to the IMO when rules and regulations have been drafted.

International Labour Organization

The ILO is the UN's specialised agency which seeks the promotion of social justice and internationally recognised human and labour rights.

It works to ensure that the safety, security and rights of the human element of any industry are safeguarded.

This means that the ILO views maritime security as part of its remit and facets of security are recognised within the Maritime Labour Convention 2006.

International Maritime Bureau

The IMB is part of the International Chamber of Commerce and is renowned for its statistical analysis and reporting on piracy matters.

Since the 1980s the IMB has been considered the pre-eminent anti-piracy organisation and its reporting centre in Kuala Lumpur has been involved in gathering vital data.

International Marine Contractors Association

IMCA has a focus on the world of offshore shipping, subsea and diving. The association's security taskforce is an innovative forum in which the largest shipowners and operators within the membership come together to develop best practice. This is then promulgated to the IMCA membership.

International Maritime Organization

The IMO is the UN's specialised agency with responsibility for the safety and security of shipping and the prevention of marine pollution by ships.

Its security role involves the development of guidelines, rules and regulations which are then the responsibility of contracting governments to enact as law for their vessels.

International Transport Workers' Federation

The ITF is an international trade union federation of transport workers' unions. Its work embraces all facets of ship and port activity and the organisation looks to ensure the rights and conditions of those employed.

This involves a security element, especially since the growth of Somali piracy has taken such a heavy toll on innocent seafarers.

Mission to Seafarers

The Mission to Seafarers provides help and support to those in need. As a Christian agency, the Mission works in more than 230 ports caring for the practical and spiritual welfare of seafarers of all nationalities and faiths.

A global network of chaplains, staff and volunteers visit seafarers on their ships offering practical help when they have problems. The Mission plays an important role in maritime security, voicing concerns over issues such as shore leave. It has also promoted a campaign to ensure that a humanitarian response to piracy is enacted. If seafarers suffer at the hands of pirates, the Mission is able to provide support and assistance.

The Nautical Institute

The Nautical Institute is the international professional body for maritime professionals, providing a wide range of services to enhance the professional standing and knowledge of members who are drawn from all sectors of the maritime world.

The work of the NI focuses on improving the safety and efficiency of shipping. There is a strong security element to this and through its IMO consultative status the NI ensures that practitioner input is heard when new rules and regulations are debated.

The NI's publications play a strong role in promoting best practice across disciplines, including maritime security. The Institute has long spoken out against the conditions of seafarers held by pirates and supports its members in bringing their plight to the attention of their national governments and policy makers. Maritime security features in its Strategic Plan 2011-2015 and this book is part of the aim of delivering practical measures to help the industry combat threats.

Regional Cooperation Agreement on Combating Piracy and Armed Robbery against Ships in Asia

ReCAAP is a regional government-to-government organisation that promotes and enhances cooperation against piracy and armed robbery in Asia. To date, 17 states have become contracting parties to ReCAAP.

The ReCAAP Information Sharing Centre (ISC) was established under the ReCAAP Agreement. The remit of ReCAAP ISC includes exchanging information among contracting parties on incidents of piracy and armed robbery, supporting capacity-building efforts of contracting parties, and developing cooperative arrangements.

Security Association for the Maritime Industry

SAMI is an organisation for private maritime security companies and related industries. It has played a leading role in creating a standard and certification programme for security providers.

Since the adoption of the ISPS Code there has been concern about the quality and experience of maritime security providers, SAMI provides reassurance and robust checks to ensure standards are applied and maintained. The organisation aims to bridge the gap between shipping and security, and has been successful at positively driving the debate concerning the use of armed guards on commercial vessels.

World Customs Organization

The WCO is the only intergovernmental organisation exclusively focused on Customs matters. With its worldwide membership, it is recognised as the voice of the global Customs community.

It is particularly noted for its work in areas covering the development of global standards, simplification and harmonisation of Customs procedures, trade supply chain security, facilitation of international trade, enhancement of Customs enforcement and compliance activities, anti-counterfeiting and media piracy initiatives, public-private partnerships, integrity promotion and sustainable global Customs capacity-building programmes.

The WCO also maintains the international Harmonised System goods nomenclature and administers the technical aspects of the WTO Agreements on Customs Valuation and Rules of Origin.

Chapter 4

Elements of the ISPS Code: roles and responsibilities

KEY ADVICE

- Introducing the key elements of ISPS Code
- Understanding the responsibilities of shipping companies, port facilities and governments
- Assessing how the code may be followed as prescribed

This chapter is intended as a brief guide to the ISPS Code. Within the code, particularly in Part B, there are lists of the minimum measures that must be taken to comply. All those involved in ship and port security activities should fully acquaint themselves with the full IMO text (available from IMO Publishing).

The ISPS Code was adopted by a diplomatic conference held 9-13 December 2002 by amending SOLAS Chapters V and XI. It came into effect on 1 July 2004. The code is divided into two parts: Part A, which is mandatory, and Part B, which gives recommendatory guidance on compliance with Chapter XI-2 and Part A.

It applies to passenger and cargo ships of 500gt and upwards, including high-speed craft, mobile offshore drilling units and port facilities serving such ships engaged on international voyages. It builds on work on maritime security previously carried out by the IMO and develops the systems management approach that has been fostered through the ISM Code by introducing the concept of risk management into the security of ships and port facilities.

Intended to provide a standardised and consistent framework for evaluating risk, the Code establishes formal processes for the identification, measurement, control and mitigation of security risks.

With the introduction of the ISPS Code, the IMO was obliged to look beyond its traditional remit and take steps to ensure security ashore as well on ships. To do this, the focus was put on the ship/port interface and the concept of the port facility (as opposed to the whole of the port) was established.

In general, the ISPS Code and amendments to SOLAS apply on land only as far as the area is an interface with a vessel. Legislation passed in the US and EU extends security provisions to the entire port, and back through the supply chain in the case of the US.

Minimum security requirements laid down include:

For ships

Company Security Officers
Ship Security Officers
Ship security assessments
Onboard security surveys
Ship security plans
Onboard management provisions and equipment

For port facilities

Port Facility Security Officers
Port facility security assessments
Port facility security plans
Shore-side management provisions and equipment

For ships and port facilities

Monitoring and controlling access
Monitoring activities of people and cargo
Ensuring security communications are readily available

As each ship (or ship type) and each port facility represents a specific level of security risk, the exact requirements of the code will be determined and approved by the administration (for ships) or contracting government (for port facilities).

In order to communicate the level of threat for a ship or at a port facility, the contracting government will set an appropriate maritime security level of the three:

Security Level 1: Normal threat
Security Level 2: Medium threat
Security Level 3: High threat

These three levels create a link between the ship and the port facility, as each level requires the implementation of appropriate security measures by both parties. As the threat increases, both ship and port facility must act to reduce vulnerabilities by providing steadily increasing safeguards.

Ships are subject to a system of survey, verification, certification and control to ensure their security measures are implemented. Port facilities are subject to inspection by government to ensure compliance with the ISPS Code. Port facility security plans (PFSPs) approved by government are submitted to IMO and include location and contact details.

Company and ship

There is a moral responsibility on the ship owner or operator to provide adequate security protection for seafarers, passengers and cargo and a commercial responsibility on the owner, operator and Master to understand the likelihood of a security breach and how best to provide practical protection within the commercial budget.

In addition to these responsibilities, the ISPS Code requires that the shipping company must, as a minimum, ensure that all its vessels comply with the requirements of Part A of the code and take into account the guidance contained in Part B in achieving this. The company has to appoint a CSO and an SSO for each of its ships, ensure that each vessel undergoes a ship security assessment (SSA) and develop an SSP for each vessel. Appropriate training must also be provided and all resources necessary for security purposes made available.

Many companies have transferred the lessons learned in complying with the ISM Code, particularly in developing a robust SMS, to their security regimes. The training, reporting and onboard resource elements all mesh well with ISPS Code requirements.

The CSO's responsibilities include ensuring that an SSA is properly carried out, that SSPs are prepared and submitted for approval and thereafter placed on board each ship.

The SSP should indicate the operational and physical security measures the ship itself should take to ensure it always operates at a minimum of Security Level 1 and the intensified measures and preparations to operate at Security Levels 2 and 3.

After satisfying the requirements of SOLAS chapter XI-2 and part A of the ISPS Code, ships will be issued with an International Ship Security Certificate (ISSC), which is retained on board and available for inspection at all times. Port state officials are permitted to inspect the SSP only if there are "clear grounds" that a vessel is not in compliance; in this case, limited access may be permitted to the specific sections of the plan relating to the non-compliance with the consent of the maritime administration of the flag state or the Master.

Under regulation XI-2/9, if there is reason to believe that the security of a ship, or the port facilities it has called at, have been compromised that ship may be subject to PSC inspections and additional control measures. The relevant authorities may request information regarding the ship, its cargo, passengers and ship's personnel prior to the ship's entry into port. Circumstances have arisen in which entry into port has been delayed and even denied.

Port facilities

Each contracting government has to ensure completion of a Port Facility Security Assessment (PFSA) for each port facility within its territory serving ships engaged on international voyages. This is essentially a risk assessment of all aspects of a port facility's operation in order to determine which parts of it are more vulnerable to attack.

As stated in The Nautical Institute publication, *Managing Risk in Shipping*, risk can be seen as the chance of an incident happening, and has two components – the frequency and the consequence.

Quantified risk assessment is the use of numerical estimates of hazards so as to make a calculated evaluation of the risks. The process involves identifying the hazards, estimating or evaluating their frequencies and consequences and then combining them to provide a measure which can be compared with other risk measures. Then depending on the outcome appropriate action can be taken.

There are many ways of presenting risk – commonly when discussing safety issues risk is divided into three categories:

Negligible – where no risk reduction measures are needed
Tolerable – where the risks should be as low as reasonably possible "ALARP"
Intolerable – where risk reduction measures must be taken irrespective of cost

For security, a slightly different view is needed as the hazards, threats and risks are man-made, and vulnerabilities need to be assessed, understood and mitigated. The formula Risk = Threats x Vulnerabilities x Impact is commonly used, and this includes an assessment of the following:

● The likelihood of a hazard event
● The vulnerability of assets to that event and
● The adverse impact of the event

The PFSA is then used to determine which port facilities are required to appoint a PFSO and prepare a PFSP. The PFSP details the operational and physical security measures the port facility will take to ensure that it always operates at a minimum of Security Level 1 and the intensified measures and preparations to operate at Security Levels 2 and 3.

Contracting governments

Responsibilities include:

● Setting applicable security levels
● Approving SSPs and amendments
● Verifying compliance of ships with SOLAS chapter XI-2 and part A of the ISPS Code
● Issuing ISSCs
● Determining which port facilities are required to designate a PFSO
● Ensuring completion and approval of PFSAs and PFSPs and amendments
● Exercising control and compliance measures
● Issuing the Statement of Compliance for port facilities
● Communicating security information to the IMO and to the shipping and port industries

Governments can designate or establish designated authorities to undertake their security duties and allow RSOs to carry out certain work with respect to ship and port facilities, but acceptance and approval of such matters remains the responsibility of the contracting government or the Designated Authority.

Obligations of the company

Depending on the number or types of ships it operates, a company may designate several persons as CSOs providing it is clearly identified for which ships each one is responsible.

The CSO's responsibilities include:

- Advising on the level of threats likely to be encountered
- Ensure SSAs are carried out
- Ensure development and implementation of the SSP
- Ensure the SSP is modified to the individual ship's security requirements
- Arrange internal audits and reviews of security activities
- Arrange verifications of the ship by the administration or the RSO
- Ensure deficiencies and non-conformities are promptly addressed
- Enhance security awareness and vigilance
- Ensure adequate security training for ship personnel
- Ensure effective communication and cooperation between the SSO and the relevant PFSOs
- Ensure consistency between security requirements and safety requirements
- Ensure that all sister-ship or fleet security plans are ship-specific
- Ensure alternative or equivalent arrangements are implemented and maintained

The Code does not impose any requirement for the rank or seniority of the person appointed to the CSO role, other than they must be in possession of a CSO qualification. However, it is implied through the job requirements that it should be someone with a heightened level of knowledge, experience and standing within the company. In many instances the role of CSO is given to the ISM designated person ashore (DPA).

Each ship must have a designated SSO, whose responsibilities include:

- Regular security inspections to ensure security measures are maintained
- Implementation of the SSP, including any amendments
- Coordinate security of cargo and ship's stores
- Propose modifications to the SSP
- Report deficiencies and non-conformities and implement corrective actions
- Enhance security awareness and vigilance on board
- Ensure provision of adequate training for shipboard personnel
- Report all security incidents
- Coordinate implementation of the SSP
- Ensure security equipment is properly operated, tested, calibrated and maintained

The Code does not specify the rank of the officer to be given this role, but it has become increasingly common practice for it to be given to a senior deck officer, either the Master or the Chief Officer, once they have completed SSO training.

In addition to appointing the CSO, SSOs and developing the security procedures which follow, the company has to ensure that the SSP contains a clear statement emphasising the Master's overriding authority and responsibility to make decisions with respect to the safety and security of the ship and to request the assistance of the company or of any contracting government as may be necessary. It must also ensure that the CSO, the Master and the SSO are given the support necessary to fulfil their duties and responsibilities.

In order to increase transparency within the industry, Part B states that the company must provide the Master with additional information, including:

- Identities of parties responsible for appointing shipboard personnel, such as
  - Ship management companies
  - Manning agents
  - Contractors
  - Concessionaries (eg retail sales outlets, casinos and caterers)
- Those responsible for deciding the employment of the ship, including time or bareboat charterers
- Contact details of charterers

The CSO must ensure that the SSA is carried out by those with appropriate skills to evaluate the security of a ship. Part B lists the areas of expert knowledge that should be available to the CSO:

- Current security threats and patterns
- Recognition and detection of weapons, dangerous substances and devices
- Characteristics and behavioural patterns of persons likely to threaten security
- Techniques used to circumvent security measures
- Methods used to cause a security incident
- Effects of explosives on ship's structures and equipment
- Ship security
- Ship/port interface business practices
- Contingency planning, emergency preparedness and response
- Physical security
- Radio and telecommunications systems, including computer systems and networks
- Marine engineering
- Ship and port operations

An SSA must include an on-scene security survey and identification of existing security measures, procedures and operations, key shipboard operations to be protected, possible threats and the likelihood of their occurrence, security weaknesses, including human factors, in the infrastructure and policies and procedures in place. The SSA for a specific ship may be carried out by an RSO.

Before commencing the SSA, the CSO must ensure that information and intelligence is available on the levels of threat posed by the ports at which the ship will call. The assessment should address the ship's physical security, structural integrity, personnel protection systems, procedural policies, radio and telecommunication systems (computer systems and networks) and other areas that pose a risk to persons, property or operations on board the ship or within a port facility.

All the information required to conduct an assessment should be obtained and recorded by the CSO, including:

- General layout of the ship
- Location of restricted access areas
- Location and function of each actual or potential access point to the ship
- Tide changes which may affect vulnerability or security of the ship
- Cargo spaces and stowage arrangements
- Locations of ship's stores and essential maintenance equipment
- Locations of unaccompanied baggage
- Emergency and stand-by equipment
- Number of ship's personnel, their security duties and training requirements
- Security and safety equipment for the protection of passengers and staff
- Escape and evacuation routes and assembly stations
- Agreements with private security companies
- Security measures and procedures

The SSA should examine each identified point of access, including open weather decks, and evaluate the potential for use by individuals who might seek to breach security. This includes points of access available to individuals having legitimate access as well as those seeking to obtain unauthorised entry.

The SSA should consider the continuing relevance of existing security measures and guidance, procedures and operations, under both routine and emergency conditions.

Security guidance

- Restricted areas
- Emergency responses
- Supervision of ship's personnel, passengers, visitors, vendors, repair technicians, dock workers, etc
- Frequency and effectiveness of security patrols
- Access control systems, including identification systems
- Security communications systems and procedures
- Security doors, barriers and lighting
- Security and surveillance equipment and systems

Protection needed for:

- Ship's personnel
- Passengers, visitors, vendors, repair technicians, port facility personnel, etc
- Safe navigation and emergency response
- Cargo, particularly dangerous goods or hazardous substances
- Ship's stores
- Ship security communication equipment and systems
- Ship's security surveillance equipment and systems

Possible threats

- Damage to or destruction of, the ship or of a port facility
- Hijacking or seizure of the ship or of persons on board
- Tampering with cargo, essential ship equipment or systems or ship's stores
- Unauthorised access or use, including presence of stowaways
- Smuggling weapons or equipment
- Use of the ship to carry those intending to cause a security incident
- Use of the ship as a weapon
- Attacks from seaward while at berth or at anchor
- Attacks while at sea

Possible vulnerabilities

- Conflicts between safety and security measures
- Conflicts between shipboard duties and security assignments
- Watchkeeping duties, number of ship's personnel, with implications for fatigue, alertness and performance
- Any identified security training deficiencies
- Any security equipment and systems, including communication systems

The CSO and SSO should always consider the effect of security measures on ship's personnel who may be onboard for long periods. This would include the convenience, comfort and privacy of the ship's personnel and their ability to maintain their effectiveness over long periods.

Upon completion of the SSA, a report is then prepared, consisting of a summary of how the assessment was conducted, a description of vulnerabilities found during the assessment and a description of counter-measures that could be used to address each vulnerability. The report must be protected from unauthorised access or disclosure.

The SSA must be documented, reviewed, accepted and retained by the company. If the SSA was not carried out by the company itself, the RSO's report of the SSA should be reviewed and accepted by the CSO.

The ISPS Code states that an on-scene ship security survey (OSS) is necessary as an integral part of the SSA process. This is an evaluation of the protective measures, procedures and operations actually in place for:

- Ensuring the performance of all ship security duties
- Monitoring restricted areas
- Controlling access to the ship
- Monitoring deck areas and areas surrounding the ship
- Controlling embarkation of persons and their effects
- Supervising handling of cargo and delivery of ship's stores
- Ensuring readily availability of ship security communication, information and equipment

It is very much a questioning process, with the aim of identifying:

- What actually happens?
- Who does what?
- What is stored where?
- How does it really work?
- When was it last done?
- How are assets protected?

A thorough survey considers all three security levels and addresses all areas of the vessel, all means of access (actual and potential), all procedures, all security equipment and all levels of activity – in all types of events.

The results of the SSA and the on-scene survey are then brought together to develop the vessel's SSP.

The SSP is the tool to solve all security issues, allowing those onboard to access the information and details of their required security responses. It must address these measures and procedures:

- To prevent unauthorised weapons, dangerous substances and devices from being taken on board
- Identify restricted areas and measures to prevent unauthorised access Prevention of unauthorised access to the ship
- Respond to security threats or breaches of security
- Respond to government security instructions at Security Level 3
- Procedures for evacuation
- Duties of shipboard security personnel
- Security activities auditing
- SSP training, drills and exercises
- Port facility security links
- Periodic review and updating of the SSP
- Reporting security incidents
- Identification of the SSO
- Identification of the CSO, including 24-hour contact details
- Ensure inspection, testing, calibration and maintenance of any security equipment on board
- Frequency of testing or calibration of any security equipment on board

- Identification of locations of ship security alert system (SSAS) activation points
- Procedures, instructions and guidance on use of the SSAS, including testing, activation, deactivation and resetting and limiting false alerts

The SSP must be protected from unauthorised access or disclosure. If kept in an electronic format, procedures must be in place to prevent its unauthorised deletion, destruction or amendment. A translation of the SSP must be available in English, French or Spanish, as well as written in the working language(s) of the ship.

As with the development of safety management systems under the ISM Code, there has been a tendency for SSPs to develop with worryingly generic contents – the result of some companies being sold 'off-the-shelf' systems. These do not provide a proper and effective SSP tailored to adequately reflect the SSA, the vessel and its trade and manning profile. In many instances, flag state officials may find fault with these as part of verification surveys as they do not reflect the realities on board the ship.

As with ISM, it is vital that companies actually do as their written procedures state and can demonstrate that this is the case.

The ISPS Code recognises that discrepancies in security provisions and perceived levels of risk will occur. To counter this, the declaration of security (DoS) has been introduced. This addresses the security requirements that could be shared between a port facility and a ship (or between ships) and will state the responsibility for security each shall take.

Contracting governments determine when a DoS is required by assessing the risk the ship/port interface or ship-to-ship activity poses to persons, property or the environment.

A ship can request completion of a DoS when:

- Operating at a higher security level than the port facility or another ship it is interfacing with
- An agreement exists on a DoS between contracting governments covering certain international voyages or specific ships on those voyages
- There has been a security threat or a security incident involving the ship or the port facility
- The ship is at a port which is not required to have an approved PFSP
- The ship is conducting ship-to-ship activities with another ship not required to have an approved SSP

Requests for the completion of a DoS must be acknowledged by the applicable port facility or ship. The DoS must be completed by the Master or SSO on behalf of the ship(s) and, if appropriate, the PFSO or, if applicable, by someone responsible for shore-side security, on behalf of the port facility.

The DoS is a vitally important tool in complying with ISPS. It is especially important as the security provisions of many port facilities globally are not of a uniform standard and vessels can protect their security integrity by completing a DoS if they are in doubt.

Where the security of a port or port facility is deemed to be below the standard required this can cause problems for a ship when calling at subsequent ports. These ports will need an assurance that the ship has maintained proper security throughout the voyage. Although not mentioned in the Code, in this case a ship will need to keep a record of the security measures taken as evidence for use at subsequent ports. The SSO or Master should therefore request the issue and agreement of a DoS using the ISPS Code format.

The keeping of security records is vital in demonstrating a vessel's compliance with ISPS.

Details of the following activities addressed in the SSP must be kept on board for at least the minimum period specified by the administration:

- Training, drills and exercises
- Security threats and incidents
- Breaches of security
- Changes in security level
- Communications relating to the direct security of the ship
- Internal audits and reviews of security activities
- Periodic review of the SSA
- Periodic review of the SSP
- Implementation of any amendments to the SSP
- Maintenance, calibration and testing of any security equipment provided on board, including testing of the SSAS

Records must be protected from unauthorised access or disclosure. If kept in an electronic format, procedures must be in place to prevent unauthorised deletion, destruction or amendment.

A translation of the records must be available in English, French or Spanish, as well as written in the working language(s) of the ship. In addition to these records, and in an attempt to add transparency to the issues of vessel ownership and control, the ISPS Code has introduced the continuous synopsis record (CSR).

Every ship to which ISPS applies will be issued with a CSR, which is intended to provide an onboard record of the history of the ship.

It must contain:

- Ship's flag
- Date of ship registration with flag state
- Ship's identification number
- Ship's name
- Port of registration
- Name of registered owner(s) and their registered address(es)
- Name of the registered bareboat charterer(s) and their registered address(es), if applicable
- Name of the company, its registered address and the address(es) from where it carries out the safety management activities
- Name of all classification societies with which the ship is classed

- Name of the administration, contracting government or RSO which has issued the document of compliance
- Name of the auditor of the DoC
- Name of the administration, contracting government or RSO that has issued the safety management certificate (SMC)
- Name of the auditor of the SMC
- Name of the administration, contracting government or RSO that has issued the ISSC, as specified in the ISPS Code
- Name of the body verifying the certificate
- Date on which the ship ceased to be registered with that state

Any changes relating to the entries must be forwarded to the administration, which will then issue a revised and updated version of the CSR. Details of these changes provide updated and current information together with the history of the changes to the vessel's status.

The CSR must be in English, French or Spanish, although a translation into the official language(s) of the administration may be provided. The CSR must be in the format developed by the IMO and maintained in accordance with IMO guidelines. Any previous entries in the CSR must not be modified, deleted, erased or defaced in any way. The CSR must be kept on board the ship and available for inspection at all times.

Security levels

The ISPS Code introduces a three-tier threat assessment system. At Security Level 1 (normal threat requiring maintenance of minimum protective security measures at all times) a ship is required to:

- Ensure performance of all ship security duties
- Control access to the ship
- Control embarkation of people and their effects
- Ensure only authorised persons have access to restricted areas
- Monitor deck areas and areas surrounding the ship
- Supervise handling of cargo and ship's stores
- Ensure that security communications are readily available

At Security Level 2 (medium threat), the additional protective measures specified in the SSP must be implemented. At Security Level 3 (high threat), further specific protective measures specified in the SSP must be implemented.

Minimum security actions for Security Level 1 are listed in Part B of the Code, plus details of the additional measures to be taken in the event of an increase in the security level.

The vessel must respond to any increase of security level by acknowledging receipt of the instructions and by implementing the necessary measures as laid down in its SSP. Before entering a port, or while in a port that has set Security Level 2 or 3, the ship must acknowledge receipt of this instruction and confirm to the PFSO that the necessary steps (as in the SSP for Security Level 2) or any additional government instructions (for Security Level 3) have been taken.

If the ship has any difficulties in implementation these must be reported and the PFSO and SSO should liaise and coordinate appropriate actions.

If a ship is at a higher security level than the port it intends to enter, or is in, the SSO must immediately advise both the government within whose territory the port is located and the PFSO. The SSO should liaise with the PFSO to coordinate appropriate actions, if necessary. If a flag state requires its ships to set Security Level 2 or 3 in a port of another contracting government it must inform that government without delay.

An area of concern has been the exact extent of a Master's powers, especially when faced with the setting of security levels. The ISPS Code clearly states that responsibility for setting the security level applying at any particular time is with contracting governments and that these levels can apply to ships and port facilities. So ships must act upon these security levels.

Circumstances can be envisaged, however, in which the Master may be forced to take rapid decisions regarding the level of security employed on the vessel before they can make contact with contracting governments. The Master may well be in a better position to assess threats to the vessel, although this does not preclude the provision of intelligence and information to the Master.

SOLAS Chapter XI-2 Regulation 8 stresses the Master's discretion for ship safety and security. Part 2 of this regulation states: "If, in the professional judgment of the Master, a conflict between any safety and security requirements applicable to the ship arises during its operations, the Master shall give effect to those requirements necessary to maintain the safety of the ship. In such cases, the Master may implement temporary security measures and shall forthwith inform the administration and, if appropriate, the contracting government in whose port the ship is operating or intends to enter. Any such temporary security measures under this regulation shall, to the highest possible degree, be commensurate with the prevailing security level. When such cases are identified, the administration shall ensure that such conflicts are resolved and that the possibility of recurrence is minimised."

This regulation means the Master can increase the security provisions onboard the vessel as a "temporary measure" and await further instruction from the contracting government as to the official security level to be adopted.

It is important to note that any such informal arrangements can only raise security levels, not lower them. The Master may have instructed personnel to act at Security Level 2 and the vessel must follow the minimum security standards laid down within the SSP for this level.

The CSO, SSO and Master should be in discussion regarding the requirements for these temporary measures and the administration should be contacted for assistance and a formal security level notification.

If a vessel is to trade into a non-compliant port it may be advisable to contact the administration prior to arrival and request the formal imposition of an increase to a minimum of Security Level 2.

Recognised security organisations

Security is treated as being outside normal shipping operations and knowledge, so to speed the adoption of the ISPS Code, a requirement for external assistance and expertise was recognised in the form of RSOs.

Contracting governments may authorise an RSO to undertake certain security related activities, including approval of SSPs and amendments, verification and certification of compliance of ships and carrying out PFSAs.

An RSO may also advise or provide assistance to companies or port facilities on security matters, including SSAs, SSPs, PFSAs and PFSPs. This can include completion of a SSA or SSP or PFSA or PFSP but in the case of an SSA or SSP, that RSO would not be authorised to approve the SSP.

Many different companies, entities and individuals have put themselves forward as RSOs, with differing degrees of success. The majority of RSO work is undertaken by the classification societies, which have bolted on a security function to their delegated flag responsibilities, and all the major IACS members have some involvement in maritime security. A number of specialised security companies have RSO status.

When authorising an RSO, consideration should be given to its competency. An RSO needs:

- Security expertise
- Knowledge of ship and port operations
- Knowledge of security risks
- Ability to minimise risks
- Maintain and improve the expertise of own personnel
- Monitor trustworthiness of own personnel
- Avoid unauthorised disclosure of, or access to, security-sensitive material
- Knowledge of the requirements of Chapter XI-2 and part A of the ISPS Code and relevant national and international legislation and security requirements
- Knowledge of current security threats and patterns
- Ability to recognise weapons, dangerous substances and devices
- Ability to recognise characteristics and behavioural patterns of persons likely to threaten security
- Knowledge of techniques used to circumvent security measures
- Knowledge of security and surveillance equipment and systems and their operational limitations

The appointment of an RSO is not a decision to be taken lightly, as any failings of the RSO can have a direct negative effect on the flag or vessel in question.

Security training and education

Training and education is a vital part of any security regime and the ISPS Code specifically states that training and drills must be conducted for all involved with security in order to hone their skills. In addition to helping crew members to perform better, training instils confidence and teaches the skills and attributes that will allow any security regime to work.

The ISPS Code requires training for the CSO and appropriate shore-based personnel and the SSO and shipboard personnel. All have specific security duties and responsibilities and training must ensure all have sufficient knowledge and ability to perform their duties. Duties within the SSP could include gangway watches, security patrolling and searching and escorting visitors.

To ensure effective implementation of the SSP, drills must be carried out at appropriate intervals taking into account the ship type, changes in ship personnel and the port facilities to be visited.

Security training and drill requirements should be reflected in the normal safety management training and STCW programmes. In addition to this specific training for personnel with security duties, all of the ship's crew should receive security awareness training as part of their general orientation and training activities.

Security awareness training should include the necessity to limit discussion about specifics of the ship operations with non-company personnel, reporting suspicious acts or behaviour on or near the ship and on shore leave and protection of company-supplied identification cards or other documentation.

Major revisions to the International Convention on Standards of Training, Certification and Watchkeeping for Seafarers (STCW Convention) and its associated Code were adopted at a Diplomatic Conference in Manila, the Philippines, in 2010. They entered into force on 1 January 2012 under the tacit acceptance procedure and include new requirements for security training, as well as provisions to ensure that seafarers are properly trained to cope if their ship comes under attack by pirates.

STCW security training

The Manila amendments introduced three levels of security training for those serving on ships that are required to comply with the ISPS Code and set out changes to the certification and competency assessments. The levels cover those who need the minimum levels of awareness, those who have an actual prescribed security role and those who are appointed to serve as an SSO.

Level one

Security awareness (all crew members)

All seafarers employed or engaged in any capacity on ships required to comply with the ISPS Code must hold a certificate of proficiency in security awareness and meet the requirements of Section A-VI/6 (Annex 2) paragraph 4 of the amended STCW Code.

The minimum standard of competence in security awareness requires:

- Improvement of maritime security through heightened awareness
- Recognition of security threats
- Understanding of the need for maintaining security awareness and vigilance and methods of achieving that

Level two

Persons with security duties

All seafarers employed or engaged in security duties on ships required to comply with the ISPS Code must hold a certificate of proficiency in designated security duties and meet the requirements of Section A-VI/6 (Annex 2) paragraph 6-8 of the amended STCW Code.

The minimum standard of competence for seafarers with designated security duties requires:

- Maintenance of the conditions set out in an SSP
- Recognition of security risks and threats
- Undertaking regular security inspections of the ship
- Proper usage of any security equipment and systems

Level three

SSOs

To serve onboard a ship as an SSO, a seafarer must complete specific approved training as required by STCW Regulation VI/5.

The minimum standard of competence for SSOs requires:

- Maintenance and supervision of the implementation of an SSP
- Assessment of security risk, threat, and vulnerability
- Regular ship inspections to ensure appropriate security measures are implemented and maintained
- Security equipment and systems are properly operated, tested and calibrated
- Encouragement of security awareness and vigilance

Company security officers

CSOs are required to have completed an approved training course. MSC/Circular 1154 provides guidelines on training and certification for CSOs.

Every person designated as a CSO should be able to demonstrate competence to undertake the tasks, duties and responsibilities in the circular and the level of knowledge of the subjects should be sufficient to enable the person to act as the designated CSO.

Persons who have satisfactorily completed an approved course based on IMO Model Course 3.20, or who have attended a course based on the knowledge, understanding and proficiencies required, should be considered to have met the requirements for service as a CSO.

The relevant knowledge, understanding and proficiencies include:

- Development, maintenance and supervision of the implementation of an SSP
- Ensuring any security equipment and systems are properly operated
- Assessment of security risk, threat and vulnerability
- Ensuring appropriate security measures are implemented and maintained
- Encouragement of security awareness and vigilance

Drills and exercises

Security drills should be planned to exercise the crew in the same way as emergency safety training, to ensure that shipboard personnel are proficient in all assigned security duties at all security levels To ensure the effective implementation of the provisions of the SSP, drills should be conducted at least once every three months. In addition, where more than 25% of the ship's complement has been changed, a drill should be conducted within one week of the change.

Drills should test individual SSP elements, such as:

- Damage to, or destruction of, the ship or port facility
- Hijacking or seizure of the ship
- Hostage-taking onboard
- Tampering with cargo, essential ship equipment or systems or ship's stores
- Unauthorised access, including presence of stowaways
- Smuggling of weapons or equipment
- Use of the ship to carry persons or equipment intended to cause a security incident
- Bomb threats
- Use of the ship itself as a weapon or as a means to cause damage or destruction
- Attacks from seaward while at berth or anchor
- Attacks while at sea

In addition, major shipboard security exercises that may include participation of company personnel and other agencies should be carried out at least once each calendar year, with no more than 18 months between the exercises.

These exercises should test communications, coordination, resource availability, and response to security incidents. Records giving details of training, drills and exercises have to be maintained as part of the mandatory ISPS requirements.

Anyone intending to act as a CSO or SSO must be in possession of the relevant qualifications and certified under the STCW Convention.

IMO guidelines indicate SSOs *must demonstrate the knowledge of the complete range of tasks, duties and responsibilities of a security officer and encourage security awareness and vigilance*. The SSO should also be able to assess security threats and risks and have full knowledge of the SSP.

As part of the CSO and SSO's responsibilities they are charged with training those on board with security skills and knowledge in relation to the duties they will be expected to perform.

To assist with the education process personnel should be made aware of:

- Security basics
- Security principles
- Security procedures
- Security levels
- Security awareness and vigilance
- Use of security equipment
- The role of personnel
- Security responses

Ship certification

During the course of its trading life every ship is subject to initial, intermediate, renewal and additional verifications. The initial verification is carried out before the ship is put into service or before an ISSC is issued for the first time. It includes a complete verification of the vessel's security system and any associated security equipment covered by the relevant provisions of SOLAS chapter XI-2, the ISPS Code and the SSP.

A minimum of one intermediate verification should take place between the second and third anniversary date of the ISSC. This includes inspection of the security system and any associated security equipment to ensure that it remains satisfactory for the service for which the ship is intended. Such intermediate verification is endorsed on the certificate.

A renewal verification is required at intervals specified by the administration, but not exceeding five years. Additional verifications can be performed as determined by the administration.

These verifications are carried out by officers of the administration but may be entrusted to an RSO. Once verification has taken place, security systems and equipment must be maintained to conform with the Code and the SSP and no changes made without the approval of the administration.

Upon successful completion of the initial verification an ISSC will be issued. This will be drawn up in a form corresponding to the model given in the appendix to the ISPS Code.

If the language used is not English, French or Spanish, the text must include a translation into one of these languages.

An ISSC is issued for a period specified by the administration, but this will not exceed five years. Extensions can be granted by an administration, up to a maximum of three months,

When the renewal verification is completed the new certificate will be valid from the date of completion of the renewal verification, even where this is before the expiry of the old certificate. If a renewal verification has been completed and a new certificate cannot be placed on board the ship before the expiry date of the existing certificate, the administration or RSO may simply endorse the existing certificate. This will only be valid for up to five months and will need to be replaced by a full ISSC.

If an ISSC expires before a ship reaches the port where it is to be verified, the administration may extend the validity period of the certificate to allow the ship to complete its voyage to this port.

An ISSC ceases to be valid if:

- Relevant verifications are not completed within the periods specified
- It is not endorsed in accordance with the Code
- A vessel undergoes a change of ownership or management
- A vessel changes flag

An interim ISSC can be issued in the last two situations, and when a ship is on delivery or prior to its entry or re-entry into service or when it changes flag from a state that is not a contracting government. To issue an interim ISSC, the administration or RSO must have verified that the SSA has been completed, a copy of the SSP is provided on board, has been submitted for review and approval, and is being implemented and that the ship is provided with an SSAS, if required.

In such cases the CSO must ensure:

- Review of the SSP for compliance
- Submission of the SSP for approval
- Implementation of the SSP on the ship
- Necessary arrangements, including drills, exercises and internal audits are in place
- The ship will complete the verification within six months
- Arrangements to carry out the verifications
- Master, SSO and other personnel with specific security duties are familiar with their duties and responsibilities and with the SSP
- SSO meets the requirements of the ISPS Code

An interim ISSC is only valid for six months or until a full certificate is issued (whichever comes first) and may not be extended. Consecutive interim certificates will not be issued if the administration or the RSO believe the intention is to avoid full compliance with SOLAS chapter XI-2 and the ISPS Code beyond the period of the initial interim certificate.

Chapter 5

Implications of the ISPS Code

KEY ADVICE

- Understanding the ISPS Code
- Understanding how crews and vessels will be assessed
- Preparing for port state security inspections
- Understanding the legal and commercial implications of security

The implications of the ISPS Code reach deep into the operations of all companies, vessels and ports. Since the introduction of the Code vessels are subject to the rigours and demands of security in addition of those of safety, and all parties involved in maritime trade have had to adapt their operations and activities to fit in with the security regimes imposed.

Commercial imperatives have still to be met and seafarers have been required to take on extra security responsibilities. The IMO has recognised that the requirements of the Code may well impose a strain on existing crewing levels, which were created to ensure and protect the safety of a vessel. Owners are compelled to ensure that the resources on board are able to cope with the wide range of new security duties and roles.

A form of security screening similar to the normal PSC targeting processes has been developed and implemented in many areas to target vessels for security risk and ISPS-related compliance examination. Additionally, information concerning last ports of call is collected and examined for possible future matrix targeting.

USCG security measures

Many of the procedures and initiatives developed by the USCG have been introduced as best practice and used in other port state regions. USCG security inspections follow the patterns established by the existing PSC regime. All vessels are screened for security and those that pose an unacceptable level of risk are boarded. Intelligence plays a major role in the assessment of the security risks posed by a vessel.

This screening uses a two-step risk-based screening tool based on security and safety. Security risk points are assessed in terms of:

- Ownership
- Flag
- RSO
- Security history
- Size
- Charterers
- Cargo
- Intelligence reports
- Trading pattern – last ports visited
- History of compliance of a vessel or port facility

In essence, the USCG is establishing a virtual US sea border, as it uses secure Internet software applications to evaluate the threat and security profile of foreign vessels before permitting them entry into port.

The approach is 'trust but verify' and involves review of internationally-issued ISSCs plus 'aggressive' onboard verification. Where non-compliance is identified the USCG acts decisively and will not hesitate to use denial of entry, expulsion from port or vessel detention.

It is not just the vessels that the US authorities take into account – the performance of owners, managers, flag states and RSOs is analysed and poor performances are widely publicised and information shared with other port states.

Integrating ISPS Code compliance into the existing PSC programme allows the USCG to address boarding and control procedures, communications and reporting and training.

PSC officers adopt a similar threshold for establishing clear grounds for security concerns as for safety issues:

- Evidence that the ISSC is invalid or expired or that the vessel has been issued with consecutive interim certificates
- Evidence of serious deficiencies in security equipment, documentation or arrangement
- Reports or complaints that a vessel does not comply with security requirements
- Evidence that the Master or key ship personnel are unfamiliar with their security duties
- Evidence that the vessel has loaded cargo, stores or persons at a non-ISPS compliant port

A USCG security inspection consists of:

- Check of certification and documentation
- Observation of security duties being carried out
- Observation of access control to vessel
- Observation of control of embarkation of persons and baggage
- Observation of control of restricted areas
- Observation of control of deck areas and areas surrounding ship

- Observation of supervision of stores and cargo handling
- Observation of availability of security communications

The USCG recognises that large parts of the vessel's SSP are restricted, hence any non-compliance will be based upon:

- The boarding officer's professional judgment
- Deficiencies in certification and documentation
- Personnel unfamiliar with security responsibilities
- Deficiencies in procedures or equipment

The USCG also asks the crew questions and will on occasions hold impromptu drills or exercises to determine whether the vessel complies with the security requirements of SOLAS, MTSA and the ISPS Code.

A number of the USCG questions posed to shipboard security personnel are detailed below, as set out in US Navigation and Vessel Inspection Circular No. 12-04: *Maritime security compliance and enforcement for US/Canadian boundary and coastal waters*.

If the SSO and other personnel can answer these questions proficiently and confidently

USCG sample questions

To the SSO

- What do you do if there is a security breach?
- What do you do if there is a security threat?
- How does the SSAS work?
- What happens if the SSAS is activated?
- What do you do if the port is at a higher security level than the ship?
- What are the vessel's restricted areas?
- How do you restrict access to these areas?
- Why do you have an interim ISSC? Is the ship new or has it re-entered service? Or has it transferred flag or owner/operator?
- How often is the security equipment calibrated? (May ask to see records)
- How do you coordinate security activities with the port facility?
- When would you limit shore-to-ship access to only one access point?
- How often do you audit security activities? How do you audit a security activity? (Will ask for an example and to see records)
- Who is the CSO?
- Do you have 24/7 contact information for this person? (May ask to see information and may try to contact the CSO to ensure details are correct)
- Do you have any active DoS?
- With whom were these DoS exchanged and why?
- How often do you hold security drills, training or exercises?
- When was the last time you conducted a security drill, training session or exercise? (May ask to see associated records)

- How do you report security breaches or incidents? (May ask to see associated records)
- What do you do if someone tries to bring an unauthorised weapon, dangerous substance or device on board the vessel?
- How do you prevent unauthorised persons from coming on board?
- Who on board are assigned security duties?
- When was the last time the SSP was reviewed?
- Was the SSP updated? (May ask to see associated records)
- How do you search persons and their belongings when they come on board?
- What are your procedures to search unaccompanied baggage?
- How do these search procedures become more rigorous if the security level increases?
- How do you monitor the security of the ship when underway?
- How do you monitor the security of the ship when alongside?
- How do you monitor the security of the ship when at anchor?
- Do you have procedures in place to bring on board additional security personnel? (Describe)
- Do you have procedures in place to ensure security for cargo handling? (Describe)
- How do you safeguard the SSP?

To crew members with security responsibilities

- Who is the SSO?
- What do you do if there is a security breach?
- What do you do if there is a security threat?
- What happens if the SSAS is activated?
- What are the vessel's restricted areas?
- How do you restrict access to these areas?
- When was the last time you participated in a security drill, training session or exercise?
- How do you report security breaches or incidents?
- What do you do if someone tries to bring an unauthorised weapon, dangerous substance or device on board the vessel?
- How do you prevent unauthorised persons from coming on board?
- How do you search persons and their belongings when they come on board?
- What are your procedures to search unaccompanied baggage?
- How do you monitor the security of the ship when underway?
- How do you monitor the security of the ship when alongside?
- How do you monitor the security of the ship when at anchor?

To crew members not having security responsibilities

- Who is the SSO?
- What do you do if there is a security threat?
- What do you do if there is a security breach?

this will play a major part in convincing the port state official that the security onboard is of the required standard.

Some questions may only be asked if the flag state has given permission to review the portion of the SSP related to that question.

Having made an initial assessment of the security of the vessel, the PSC officer will conduct a documentary check. It is vital that such a check is done in as professional a manner as possible. The SSO (or whoever is assisting the PSC officer) should have all necessary documentation available and it should be presented in a neat, organised and systematic way.

Non-compliance will subject a vessel to a range of control and compliance measures. If a vessel is of particular concern, control measures may be exercised prior to port entry. The USCG has stressed on numerous occasions the concept of screening and targeting and enormous resources have been made available to the USCG to enable it to adequately assess the identity of the vessels coming into its waters and decide if further action is required.

A vessel may be ordered to wait outside port limits until such action as deemed necessary by the security forces is taken.

The USCG states it is seeking to impose 'aggressive enforcement' and 'visible accountability' – highlighting the burden implementing security measures places on those on vessels. SSOs, CSOs and crews need to do all they can to prove to the port state authorities that they are compliant on paper and in practice.

Vessels not in compliance will be denied entry to the US. In addition, any vessel found not compliant with ISPS, or unable to prove compliance, will be subject to any of the following penalties:

- Cargo operations will cease and the vessel may be forced to proceed out-bound until further notice
- Additional security from an outside source may be required
- The vessel may be refused entry to the port
- The crew will be placed under a security quarantine. This may include the vessel's agent
- The vessel will have to contact its flag state informing it of the control action, and this may result in a SOLAS detention in the next port.

If in port, the USCG may require expanded examination of the ship's security procedures, restrict its movement, detain it or expel it from port. Prior to arrival the USCG may delay or deny entry.

There is now a requirement for an advance Notice of Arrival (NOA) to be provided to the USCG and this is mirrored in many other jurisdictions. This requires information on whether or not a vessel has an ISSC.

Authorities will also need to be informed of:

- Details of the security level at which the ship is operating
- Security level at which it operated in the last 10 ports of call
- Any special or additional security measures undertaken at the last 10 ports of call
- Confirmation that appropriate procedures were maintained during any ship-to-ship activity between the last 10 ports of call
- Records of any DoS agreements at the last 10 ports of call and other practical security-related information

If it passes the verification, the vessel will be issued with a letter stating that it is approved and ISPS-compliant. This letter does not expire and will not be re-issued unless deficiencies are noticed on random boarding. The vessel must always be able to prove it is ISPS-compliant.

The USCG reviews every case involving an ISPS-related detention, expulsion or denial of entry and determines whether the action or inaction of the RSO contributed to the control action. A set of guidelines has been established by the Coast Guard Office of Compliance (G-MOC-2) to determine and apportion such culpability.

As a result, RSOs will be targeted based on the total number of related major control actions accumulated during the previous 12-month period as determined by USCG HQ. In the event that the USCG identifies any control actions with a specific RSO, any vessels that have been associated with this RSO may also be exposed to control actions.

International port state regimes

Since July 2004 the Committee of the Paris MOU has introduced a *focused harmonised* action plan to inspect all ships subject to the provisions of the ISPS Code. In the light of the lead taken by the USCG, many other PSC regimes have followed much of the example set by the US authorities.

It is worth highlighting that if a vessel's security planning, manning and procedures are robust enough to satisfy the USCG, it should be capable of convincing any PSC inspection of its ISPS capabilities.

Regardless of the actual tactics that the various PSC regimes pursue, the key elements to be considered by PSC officers include:

- Valid ISSC on board
- Control of access to the vessel
- Control of access to sensitive areas of the ship
- Vessel's security level (in comparison to the security level of the port facility)
- Holding of records of the last 10 ship-to-port or ship-to-ship interfaces
- Security drills and exercises carried out at required intervals, taking account of crew changes
- Master and ship's personnel appear to be familiar with essential ship security procedures

- Effective communication between key members of the ship's personnel
- Whether a subsequent interim ISSC has been issued to avoid full compliance with ISPS
- Ship identification number permanently marked in a visible place

If deficiencies are recorded against any of these, the PSC officer or competent security authority may take action.

As with the US system, a port state arrival screening regime is in place in which contracting governments assess classification of security threats, safety compliance and security compliance.

The traditional PSC boarding scope is largely unchanged but now includes an additional security focus. Initially this will consist of the PSC officer's observations of security practices in place and a review of ISPS-related documents and certificates.

The ISSC is accepted as *prima facie* evidence of ISPS compliance unless there are 'clear grounds' that the ship is not in compliance, including:

- Expired or invalid ISSC
- Evidence of serious security equipment, documentary or procedural deficiencies
- Personnel assessed as being unfamiliar with their security duties
- Receipt of credible reports or complaints that the vessel does not comply
- Ineffective communication between personnel with security responsibilities
- Evidence that the vessel has embarked people, stores or goods from a non-ISPS compliant source without signing a DoS or taking any additional security measures
- Vessel has been issued with consecutive interim ISSCs

If clear grounds for non-compliance are established, PSC officials are authorised to impose controls on the vessel. In the first instance, they will attempt to establish communications with the ship and its administration in order to rectify the situation. Should this fail, they may then take proportionate control measures, such as the *Recommended Control Measures* published by the UK's Maritime and Coastguard Agency for PSC officers.

These include:

- Inspection of the vessel
- Requirement to rectify the non-compliance
- Delay of the vessel
- Denial of entry into port
- Detention of the vessel
- Restriction of operations, including movement within the port
- Expulsion from port

The contracting government may also apply alternative or additional lesser administrative or corrective measures.

The UK recommended control measures includes this guidance given to port state control officers and the responses to specific common infringements	
General security aspects	
Ship operating at lower security level than port	Rectify immediately
No records of training drills	Rectify before departure
No record of last 10 ship-port (or ship-ship) interfaces	Rectify before departure
Key members of ship security personnel unable to communicate effectively on security matters	Rectify before departure
ISSC	
No valid ISSC (discovered during inspection)	Detention
No valid ISSC (ship fails flag state/RSO verification)	Detention
ISSC issued by unfamiliar RSO	Confirm authenticity
Access control to ship	
Inappropriate access controls to ship	Rectify immediately
Not checking identity of all persons seeking to board	Rectify immediately
No separation of checked and unchecked passengers and baggage (passenger ship)	Rectify immediately
No separation of embarking and disembarking passengers (passenger ship)	Rectify immediately
Restricted areas	
Restricted areas not marked	Rectify before departure
Access to restricted areas not controlled	Rectify before departure
Access to bridge and engine room unable to be locked	Rectify before departure
Access to bridge and engine room uncontrolled	Rectify immediately
Monitoring security of ship	
No deck watches in place or surveillance equipment in use	Rectify immediately
No monitoring seaward or landwards approaches	Rectify immediately

Delivery of stores	
No checking methods for signs of tampering before loading	Rectify immediately
No checking methods against stores order on loading	Rectify immediately
No methods of securing stores once loaded	Rectify immediately
Unaccompanied baggage	
No screening or searching in place	Rectify immediately

Making a good impression

In preparing for a port state security inspection, attention to a number of factors will better position a vessel to demonstrate its security compliance and the effectiveness of its security regimes. Making a positive first impression will have a strong beneficial effect on the rest of the inspection. Visual indicators of security include:

- Access control
- Lighting
- Cameras
- Signage
- Personnel activity
- Alarm detectors, etc

In practice, PSC security inspections are fairly limited, but they will include:

- Viewing the gangway watch
- Assessing the understanding of the SSP shown by the Master, SSO and other key personnel
- Testing awareness of the identity of the CSO
- Sighting a valid ISSC or interim ISSC
- Checking that security equipment is functional

PSC officers may note a deficiency if any of the following is observed:

- Gangway not manned
- Visitors not checked in, including PSC personnel
- Access area control low or non-existent
- Poor monitoring of decks and surrounding areas
- Unmanned stores or personal effects
- Crew do not know who is coming on board
- Crew do not know who is their designated SSO
- Original cargo documents not on board
- Vessel staff cannot prove she is ISPS-compliant
- Crew unfamiliar with SSP and related procedures

If a PSC officer can board the vessel unchallenged this will obviously not make a good impression and will lead to a closer scrutiny of the SSP. It is therefore essential that crew members are trained to carry out an effective gangway watch where visitors are stopped and asked to identify themselves and to state their business.

This is not as easy as it sounds, as crew members of some nationalities are reluctant to stop visitors, especially those in uniform. It has also been reported that the appointed officials (including port state, Customs and Immigration and police) of some countries have been particularly heavy-handed in their attempts to board vessels and have even refused to supply identification.

In such instances, security training should ensure the gangway watchman is aware of the correct and required response and also of the responsibilities and responses within the SSP. As a minimum, advice would be to keep the officials under supervision at the gangway until the SSO or a senior officer can be brought to the scene to assist.

If the officials still refuse to comply with the requirements of the vessel and the need to supply identification they should be denied access. The vessel should also seek shore assistance from the PFSO in such circumstances. Most agencies have now issued guidelines to personnel informing them of the need to assist vessels to comply, rather than trying to force failures upon them.

If at any time a vessel is boarded or viewed by PSC and it is noted that the vessel's security is not conducted in accordance with basic ISPS regulations, the PSC officer will ask to see the SSP. At no other time can the PSC officer see the SSP unless prior approval is sought from the flag state. There is no right to request to see the SSP until a deficiency is noticed or anticipated. In such an event, the PSC officer may only be granted access to the section of the SSP to which the perceived non-conformity applies.

The SSP must be stored securely together with any copies in existence. Should the plan be out and available to anyone, the vessel will be subject to immediate strict control measures.

As the SSP must be maintained "current and applicable" to the vessel's trading pattern and routes, there must be provision within the vessel's security regime for accessing contemporary threat information. Without this, a PSC officer could deem the SSP to be non-compliant.

The SSP is also required to have within it details of the security records specified in the Code (see Chapter 4). Failure to maintain the SSP in this way will contribute to the possibility of detention or delay. Having an approved SSP does not mean that it is still current and valid but simply that the SSP was in compliance with the requirements at the time of approval.

Ten common ship security PSC deficiency areas:

- Valid or original ISSC not on board; details do not match ISM SMC and DOC
- Access control procedures not in accordance with SSP and ISPS Code
- Inadequate Master/SSO familiarity with overall SSP, including its basic provisions, measures and procedures
- Inadequate crew familiarity with own ISPS roles and responsibilities
- Restricted area marking and control not in accordance with SSP
- Inadequate security record-keeping in terms of currency and completeness
- Ship-port interface (DoS) not well understood or documented (including coordination efforts and performance between SSO and PFSO)
- Blind trust in SSAS and general lack of technical knowledge
- Sub-standard attitude and awareness evidenced by complacency and denial, lack of openness with PSC and general lack of awareness of composite effects in PSC targeting
- The emphasis awarded to certain criteria, including owner/operator, flag, charterer, RSO, classification society, ship type and age and inspection/detention history should also be borne in mind as any of these are likely to attract PSC attention to a vessel

Source: DNV reports, 2009

Legal and commercial implications of maritime security

The maritime industry has evolved and refined its rules, laws and traditions over centuries, but with security and the ISPS Code, shipping has been faced with managing a wholly alien set of constraints.

The commercial implications and consequences of maritime security are complex and potential costly. Parties that feel they may be commercially affected by any elements of security should ensure they access the latest advice from their P&I clubs and lawyers.

The commercial and operational needs of companies, ships, ports and international trade were not a priority when drafting or subsequently applying the ISPS Code.

Regardless of the causes, the commercial implications of security rest on the age-old questions: who will pay? and how can costs be reduced? Owners will want charterers to pay for any delays, and vice versa.

In terms of practical measures to reduce delays and their consequences, the emphasis for owners should be on preparation. Owners may wish to make enquiries of local port agents as soon as charterers give voyage instructions in order to see if there are any specific local requirements, risks or problems at that particular port and to see if any obvious delays are likely. The CSO should liaise with the PFSO in any event.

The requirements within the Code for additional information and documentation to be made available by owners can occasionally cause difficulty. In addition to the CSR, the company is obliged under Regulation XI – 2/5 to provide the Master with the following information:

- Who decides the employment of the shipboard personnel?
  This could include: ship management companies, manning agents and contractors. On passenger vessels this will extend to concessionaries (retail sales outlets, casino staff and hotel services)
- Who decides the vessel's employment?
  Including time or bareboat charterers or any other entity acting in such a capacity
- Contact details of all charterers
  Where the vessel is employed under a charterparty, the contact details will encompass all parties, such as time or voyage charterers.

These requirements are likely to generate additional paperwork and complication and to comply with them owners must be aware of all within the chartering chain – from charterers to sub-charterers. The obvious way to achieve this would be for charterparties to contain a clause requiring charterers to notify owners or their immediate head-owners of any sub-charters entered into. All charterparties in the chain would have to contain comparable back-to-back clauses.

Due in no small part to the very guarded nature of shipping, the requirement of notification of those deciding the employment of the ship, is likely to be especially awkward – as the particular 'party' is likely to be difficult to identify. Is this the person or company who enters into charterparties on behalf of the shipowning company? Is it the charterer? Or is it cargo interests, who dictate where they want the cargo to be shipped?

In the case of a voyage charter, as long as the discharge port is specified in the charterparty, the person who decides where the ship goes is more clearly likely to be the charterer. The answer is less straightforward in the case of a timecharter or a tramping ship, or where a cargo is sold during the voyage.

Timecharters

The question of who bears the cost of any delay is obviously the key question in relation to timecharterers. In order to avoid disputes it would be prudent for owners to deal with the allocation of the cost of delay and other costs, including the expense of raising security levels, within the charterparty.

BIMCO has tackled the issue with an ISPS Code clause for timecharter parties.

This principally provides that owners shall ensure that both the vessel and the company (as defined by the ISPS Code) comply with the requirements of the code.

Owners must be capable of providing a copy of the relevant ISSC (or an interim certificate) to the charterers.

The owners must provide the charterers with the full contact details of the CSO. The charterers shall provide the CSO and the SSO or Master with their full contact details and the contact details of all sub-charterers.

Any failures on the part of the owners or the company to comply with the requirements of the ISPS Code which result in loss, damage, expense or delay will be for the owners' account. While losses, damage, expense or delays caused by failure on the part of the charterers to comply with this proposed clause will be for the charterers' account.

All delay, costs or expenses arising out of or related to security regulations or measures required by the port facility in accordance with the ISPS Code shall be for the charterers' account, unless such costs or expenses result solely from the owners' negligence.

Voyage charters

The effect of the ISPS Code on voyage charters can be summed up in a basic question: Do ISPS-related delays count as laytime or demurrage? The main concern is the start of laytime and when a ship is deemed to have "arrived" for the purposes of giving a Notice of Readiness (NOR).

Where port authorities attempt to improve security by minimising the number of vessels at anchor, vessels may be instructed to wait some distance outside port limits, as often happens off West African ports. This can create delays entering port, so scheduling ship movements can be difficult.

It has been held by the UK High Court (in the case of the *Johanna Oldendorff*, 1973) that where a vessel has been ordered to wait outside the port by the port authority, it is not an 'arrived ship'.

The responsibility for the likely delay and expense as a consequence of this would fall upon owners under many current charterparties. Owners may therefore wish to include a provision in the voyage charter for the risk of delay to be transferred to the voyage charterers in such circumstances.

In circumstances where a vessel is already an 'arrived ship' but is later detained or removed due to ISPS Code provisions, presumably, laytime would continue to run unless the charter specifically stated that ISPS-related delays were not to count.

Owners could try to get charterers to include a clause in the voyage charter such as the BIMCO US Security Clause. This states that unless caused by owners' negligence, any delay suffered or time lost in obtaining entry and exit clearances to a US port shall count as laytime or time on demurrage. It is debatable whether charterers would agree to such clauses.

Control actions

The identity of the charterers can have an effect on the reception a vessel receives as it nears or enters a port. Many port states actively check the identities of vessels, their trading patterns, crews, cargoes, owners, managers and charterers to assess the degree of risk they pose. A charterer that causes concern to the authorities, for whatever reason, may lead to control and compliance measures being enacted against a vessel.

One major problem from a legal and commercial perspective is that the information and intelligence that a government acts upon in such an instance is sensitive and none of the parties to the decision or control action may be aware of why it has been taken.

Port-related costs

Under a voyage charter port costs are usually for owners' account. However, from the owners' perspective, it is unfair and undesirable to pay for additional port costs arising out of security measures taken under the ISPS Code. It is advisable therefore to include provision in the voyage charter for allocation of such costs.

There might also be additional costs relating to cargo security. Again, there is no reason why owners should automatically bear such costs. Owners should therefore also consider including a provision that any ISPS costs relating to cargo (eg the cost of any additional security required by the port) should be for charterers' account.

Safe port warranties

The obvious question is does a heightened level of security under the ISPS Code make a port unsafe?

Law firm Stephenson Harwood explained the usual interpretation of a safe port warranty (whether express or implied) in a time or voyage charterparty. At the time of nomination of the port it should be considered safe for the period of the vessel's likely visit, in the absence of some abnormal or unexpected future event. The key consideration will be whether the threat of terrorism is capable of making a port prospectively 'unsafe'.

The question for shipowners will be whether or not they have the right to reject voyage instructions when the port nominated by charterers is either operating at Security Level 3 or 2 at the time of nomination. There are obvious implications that a port at Security Level 3 under the ISPS Code could by definition be 'unsafe'.

The test as to whether a shipowner is justified in rejecting voyage instructions on the basis that a port is 'unsafe' is that of what a 'reasonable' shipowner would do in the circumstance and was laid down in the case of the *Saga Cob* in 1992. In this case, the UK Court of Appeal did not find the particular port to be unsafe just because there was reported guerrilla activity on land. The Court of Appeal concluded: "[The port] will not be regarded as unsafe unless the 'political' risk is sufficient for a reasonable shipowner or Master to decline to send or sail his vessel there".

It may be that such questions are rendered redundant, as it is doubtful that port authorities will allow normal port movements to continue, and so it is unlikely that a vessel will be allowed to enter a port during a Level 3 alert.

War risk and contracts of carriage

Owners could be faced with problems if they refuse to go to a port when it is at Security Level 3. According to *War Risk and Contracts of Carriage* by Stig Gregersen, Jørgen Rasch and Anders Ulrik (September 2001), when considering whether they are justified in refusing to go to a certain port when it is at Security Level 3, owners should also consider other clauses of the charterparty. Many standard forms have printed clauses that give the owners the right not to perform the intended voyage – for example, Voywar 1993 and War Cancellation Clause (for voyage charter parties) and Conwartime 1993 and War Cancellation Clause (for time charterparties).

These clauses provide that where owners reasonably consider that the vessel is likely to be exposed to 'war risks' (the definition of which includes acts of terrorism and which may cover certain elements of piracy), they are entitled to reject charterers' voyage instructions and call for new ones, failing which owners may be able to legitimately, and more easily, terminate the charter party.

What happens if a port is operating at Level 1 on nomination by charterers and subsequently security increases to Level 2 or 3? Under a timecharter, if owners decide, having considered all circumstances objectively, that the port is "unsafe", the timecharterers will generally be obliged to nominate an alternative safe port.

However, under a voyage charter, if the voyage charterer has nominated a safe port in the charter and that port subsequently becomes unsafe, the voyage charterer is not obliged to make an alternative nomination. Unless there is express provision in the charterparty dealing with such a situation, the vessel would either have to proceed to the nominated port in spite of it being 'unsafe' or wait until the port is considered to be 'safe' once more.

In such circumstances, the delay could conceivably be excessive enough to frustrate the voyage charter. It would therefore be sensible to consider inserting clauses into a voyage charter dealing with what should happen in such a case – for example, obliging charterers to make an alternative nomination. In the absence of such an alternative nomination, owners could be permitted to sail to an alternative 'safe port' at their discretion.

The question of whether a ship could be expected to enter ports at Security Level 2, or 3 may be proved academic by the contracting government of the port, as it may simply not allow any vessels to enter, regardless of the contents of their charterparties.

Direct costs

One of the most difficult issues is measuring the benefits of security measures through cost-benefit analysis. Companies that have made large investments in security require better information about the returns, just as with any other investments.

The Somali piracy threat highlights the decision-making process that owners often face. These decisions have to be based on intelligence and data on whether to avoid risk (not sending ships to certain high risk areas), transfer the risk (through insurance), or to increase the security provisions on board.

The problem is the lack of clear means of assessing the value of different security measures. The only way to fully assess the return on investment is to gauge it against the number of pirate or terrorist attacks, or against the potential business costs of not being able to trade into the likes of the US, EU and Japan.

The disquiet and concerns which have stemmed from the ISPS Code and its commercial implications are similar to the fear and uncertainty that followed the inception of the Oil Pollution Act of 1990 and the ISM Code. Many felt initially it was impossible to comply with such anti-pollution and safety demands, but years down the line OPA 90 and ISM requirements are accepted as a normal cost of business. The same patterns have slowly been applied to security issues also.

The only answer for owners is to promptly and adequately prepare themselves and throw sufficient resources behind their efforts – with financial and HR investment, security requirements can be absorbed into normal operations. It is vital to remember that nothing can be made 100% secure while maintaining its full operational capability – so it is necessary to manage and balance security responsibilities with the need to remain commercially viable.

ISPS and other commercial parties

It is important that seafarers and shipowners appreciate the areas of security responsibility that other parties may face.

The International Transport Intermediaries Club (ITIC), the specialist insurer for transport professionals, has issued some sound advice to those involved on the periphery of the ISPS Code provisions, as the security legislation has had a considerable effect on port agents, chartering brokers, technical managers and commercial managers.

Port agents

While the functions and duties of port agents are not specifically referred to in the ISPS Code, they are an important link between the ship, the company and the port facility.

Security issues involving port agents include:

- Obtaining, maintaining, and disseminating up-to-date information on the security levels of ships due to call under their agency and the port facilities in the agent's area that those ships will call at. Agents should at all times be aware not only of the current security level of the port facilities in which they operate but also of all the ships for which they are the agent

- As good practice, port agents should also maintain a handbook containing the identity of all PFSOs, together with telephone numbers (landline and mobile), fax numbers and email addresses

- Prior to the ship's arrival the agent will need to:

    i) Provide to the ship contact details of the PFSO and to the port facility details of the SSO

    ii) Inform the ship of the pre-arrival security information required by the port facility (eg previous 10 ports called at and their security levels) and the time period in which it has to be provided

    iii) Pass on the pre-arrival security information to the port facility, coastguard and Customs (as appropriate in the agent's port) within the time allowed

    iv) Obtain from the ship full details of cargo, dangerous cargo, crew and other persons on board. Usually the port facility will provide a form to be filled out by the ship. The agent should instruct the ship to send the information electronically if possible as it takes time to re-type information received by fax. Faxes are only available during working hours and transcribing information can result in errors

- Liaising between the ship and the port facility. All communications received by the port agent should be passed on accurately and without delay. Where made by telephone, a written note should be kept recording the salient information and it would be good practice to keep a separate notebook specifically for this purpose

- Liaising between the ship and the local authorities (coastguard, Customs authorities and port). In some jurisdictions legislation has been passed which makes the agent jointly and severally liable for fines resulting from breaches of regulations relating to the ISPS Code. Even before the implementation of the ISPS Code, agents in the US were fined as a result of a failure by the ship to send the NoA to the US Coast Guard with details of crew, passengers and cargo within the time period allowed

- Maintaining confidentiality of such security information as is provided to the agent

- Ensuring that all agency personnel and all visitors (eg surveyors) are in possession of a valid photo ID issued by the appropriate authority recognised by the port facility. The implementation of the ISPS Code severely restricts the physical access of individuals to areas within port facilities and ships within the port, especially when security levels are increased to levels 2 and 3

- Assisting the ship if there is a DoS. The port agent may need to operate as the communication channel between the SSO and the PFSO

- The port agent may also need to communicate with the designated authority of a contracting government, particularly in connection with information required by the latter in determining whether a ship has fulfilled all the required conditions of entry into a specific port

Practical security-related information contained in the ISPS Code which should reasonably be known by the port agent includes:

- Location of the ship at the time the report is made
- Expected time of arrival of the ship in port
- Crew list
- General description of cargo
- Passenger list

Although there is no legal requirement under the ISPS Code for anyone other than the ship, the company and the port facility to appoint a security officer, the ITIC recommends that it is good practice for one or two agency personnel to be given overall responsibility for ISPS Code matters to ensure that there is an adequate understanding of the requirements, that specific instructions from customers are properly handled and to interact with the PFSO in order to be on top of security issues. This person or persons should also attend meetings on ISPS matters organised by the port facilities with which they have dealings.

A closely coordinated relationship between the Master or CSO and SSO and their appointed port agent can make any port call work smoothly and mitigate the commercial risks posed to the vessel. It is important that the value and extent of this relationship is recognised by all parties. It makes sense for security and as port agents look to secure repeat custom it makes sense for business too.

Ship managers

The CSO is responsible for ensuring that the ship's security assessment is carried out and the SSP is prepared.

In entering a management agreement it may be that the ship manager will be providing the CSO for the vessel or fleet in question, as required under the ISPS Code. The duties and responsibilities of the CSO are set out in paragraph 11 of Part A of the Code and covered in this book.

Commercial managers

A commercial manager with authority to fix a vessel and cargo charters will have to keep a record of the ports to which the ship has traded. The ship has to maintain on board a list of its last 10 calls at port facilities, whether the port facilities were ISPS-compliant, and at what level.

In addition, it is a requirement of the Code that there are details on board the ship not only of the charterer for the current voyage but also the timecharterer and any sub-voyage charterers in the chain leading to the current voyage charterer.

This does not mean that the commercial manager is responsible to the shipowner if the ship has problems at any particular port but an extra degree of care will have to be used to obtain the owner's authority to call at non-compliant ports or to notify the owner of the potential problems in calling at compliant ports when a non-compliant port has been called at within the previous 10 port calls.

It will, naturally, be impossible for the company to ensure that the ports at which the ship calls have security levels that are compatible with the ports that it is expected to call at, but an awareness of the potential problems of calling at "rogue ports" is important.

An example would be of the changing status of some ports. For instance the Côte d'Ivoire and Comoros were added to US Federal Register in 2011 and vessels entering US after calling at designated nations must implement security measures.

The two African nations join a list of other countries against which such restrictions apply including Cambodia, Cameroon, Cuba, Equatorial Guinea, Guinea-Bissau, Indonesia, Iran, Liberia, Madagascar, São Tomé and Principe, Syria, Timor-Leste and Venezuela.

A vessel or company has no say in the security level set by a port. All that the Master or CSO and SSO can do is ensure that their SSP and flag state instructions are correctly adhered to and that a DoS is exchanged if necessary. The commercial manager must appreciate these procedures when faced with a vessel calling into a potential 'problem' port facility.

Armed guards and the use of force

Numerous legal and commercial questions arise when use of armed guards is considered. Uppermost is the question of whether armed guards or chartered escort boat can use lethal force, and if they do, what is the liability for the owner?

In the UK 'lethal force' is normally only allowed where there is serious and imminent threat to life. The decision to use lethal force must be reasonable and the force used proportionate. The Security Association for the Maritime Industry (SAMI) has led industry developments on a standardised set of Rules for the Use of Force. This is the 100 Series rules, which have been tested by lawyers and stakeholders across shipping.

Distinguishing between fishermen armed to protect themselves and pirates intent on hijacking a vessel should be possible – but perhaps only at the last moment. There has undoubtedly been at least one incident where an armed security team has engaged a fishing boat with devastating effect.

Where the flag state authorises or directs the presence on board of military personnel, these issues may well be more straightforward.

There is some movement in this area in the US, where proposals have been made that immunity against prosecution should be given to those who injure or kill a pirate while protecting a ship from attack.

According to advice issued by Ince & Co, there are a range of parties who should be involved in any decisions on the use of armed guards. These include insurers, cargo interests and charterers.

Insurers

The use of armed guards should be discussed and agreed with all underwriters. Lawyers envisage arguments that the practice may affect the validity of a policy and the recoverability of a claim under a valid policy. Arguably, this could be the case even if the security providers were on board with underwriters' full agreement. Where a voyage through pirate high risk areas requires a variation of a policy (for example because it involves a change of trading limits), then disclosure considerations also apply.

Cargo interests

Damage arising from, or caused by, the use of armed forces (particularly if the use of that force was negligent or illegal) may give rise to an argument under the bill of lading contract that the vessel was unseaworthy. Informing cargo interests of the intention to arm the vessel should therefore be considered.

Charterers

The security providers are likely to want to agree a route prior to transit of a high risk area. That route may not be the normal or quickest route and may represent a deviation or a failure to use utmost dispatch under the relevant charterparty. An unauthorised deviation may mean a breach of the charter or contract of carriage which could then jeopardise the P&I cover. There may also be off-hire implications. Interesting questions could arise, for example, if the vessel was taken by pirates while deviating. What happens if someone is killed or the ship or cargo is damaged during a hijack as a result of the actions of the guards?

The security contracts may have a 'knock-for-knock' type provision, which means that in the event that a guard or crew member is killed without negligence occurring, then the loss falls where it lies and there is no recourse between owner and the security company. The security company should have some kind of public liability insurance to cover it in cases where there has been negligence. That may not prevent owners being sued by dependants or cargo interests if they think there is fault or some other breach (such as the duty of care under an employment contract) on the part of owners.

Anecdotal evidence suggests that there have been attempts to persuade P&I clubs to agree to treat guards as supernumeraries and therefore covered as if they were crew.

Standard contract

As the use of contract private security increases, the Baltic and International Maritime Council (BIMCO) has produced a standardised contract between shipowners and private maritime security companies called "Guardcon". This provides clarity on a range of key issues and includes standards to which the Contractor (PMSC) must conform in terms of:

- Providing adequate insurance to cover their liabilities and contractual indemnities (which shipowners should verify)
- Having in place the necessary permits and licences to allow them to lawfully transport and carry weapons
- Liability and indemnity provisions based on knock for knock principles
- The Master's responsibility for the safe navigation and overall command of the vessel

Customs, movement of arms

Another problematic issue surrounding the use of PMSCs and PCASP has been the Customs-related aspects of the carriage, embarkation and disembarkation of PCASP firearm and security equipment.

The IMO is working with the World Customs Organization (WCO) to ensure that the problems and issues of the safe, secure and legal movement of weapons is addressed. This work is ongoing as there are a number of complex political aspects to be managed.

Armed fleets

A number of companies have developed businesses providing proactive physical protection for vessels transiting pirate-infested waters. The various convoy escort options provide armed patrol boats in the Gulf of Aden, with crews consisting mainly of ex-military personnel trained to intercept pirates before they can hijack vessels. Market sources hint that such fleets are set to grow in popularity, as providers look to exploit the need of vessels for security and the problems facing naval forces looking to provide effective cover for the whole region. The use of armed private fleets may bring with them some unexpected advantages.

There have been arguments that one of the difficulties the naval powers have in tackling the pirates is the very nature of asymmetric warfare. Huge powerful vessels, thousands of people, with their long and traditional command and control structures do not work well when faced with lithe, flexible opponents.

It seems that the pirates are able to evolve and adapt their tactics very successfully while the armed forces are left to follow the same track for too long. All too often the failure to adapt, or the delay in evolving tactics, gives the upper hand to the pirates.

The armed flotilla approach could offer a potentially unexpected bonus in the war on piracy. The independent, private nature of the fleet will perhaps lessen the asymmetric advantage that the pirates are so adept at using.

By loosening the shackles of the response to piracy, albeit within the bounds of the law, it may be possible to take the fight to the pirates on a more equal and effective footing.

Chapter 6

Security and seafarers

KEY ADVICE

- Understanding how security affects seafarers
- Understanding shore leave entitlement
- Understanding identification issues
- Planning for increased workload and unfamiliar roles
- Dealing with violence against seafarers
- Understanding issues of command and control

Making shipping secure has had a significant effect on all within the maritime industry but especially so on seafarers actually manning vessels.

Whereas the IMO is responsible for the regulatory framework of shipping, the International Labour Organization (ILO) is the UN specialised agency responsible for drawing up and overseeing international labour standards.

It is the only tripartite UN agency, bringing together representatives of governments, employers and workers to jointly shape policies and programmes promoting decent work for all. This tripartite structure gives an equal voice to each of the three parties to ensure the views of all are closely reflected in labour standards and in shaping policies and programmes.

At a maritime session held in February 2006 at Geneva in Switzerland, the Maritime Labour Convention (MLC), 2006 was adopted by the International Labour Conference of the ILO under article 19 of its constitution.

Although not directly related to security, this sets out seafarers' rights to decent conditions of work and helps to create a basis for fair competition for shipowners. It is intended to be globally applicable, easily understandable, readily updatable and uniformly enforced. MLC is often referred to as the "fourth pillar" of the international regulatory regime for quality shipping, complementing SOLAS, STCW and MARPOL.

The link to SOLAS and welfare standards means there is no ignoring MLC when it comes to the effect security has on people working on vessels and within ports. MLC has prompted a renewed focus on the effect on seafarers which had been highlighted in resolution 11 of the diplomatic conference that adopted the amendments to SOLAS. This stated that governments should afford special protection to seafarers and remember the critical importance of shore leave when implementing the ISPS Code. It also encouraged governments, member states and non-governmental organisations to report to IMO any instances where the human element has been adversely impacted by implementation.

Measures to implement the amendments to SOLAS and the ISPS Code must be consistent with proper respect for fundamental rights and freedoms as set out in international instruments, particularly those relating to maritime workers and refugees.

The Convention on Facilitation of International Maritime Traffic (FAL) 1965 provides that foreign crew members be allowed ashore by the public authorities while their ship is in port (provided that the formalities of immigration have been fulfilled and there are no concerns relating to public health, safety or order). Since ship's personnel live and work on the vessel, they need shore leave and access to shore-based seafarer welfare facilities, including medical care.

Despite these provisions and requirements, the threat remains to the right to shore leave, that most time-honoured of maritime customs, as ports around the world increase their security provisions. There have been a number of cases in which seafarers have found themselves confined to their vessels.

Immigration authorities in many counties are significantly tightening security checks because of the threat of terrorism but also in order to detect economic migrants and asylum seekers. Visa waivers are now a thing of the past and crew members, with or without visas, are often kept on board.

It is to be hoped that MLC will clearly demonstrate that shore leave is a vital element of life at sea in terms of living and working conditions.

Identification issues

Another major problem is the authentication of seafarer identities. The shipping labour market is, by its very nature, truly global and this apparently causes fear and uncertainty within some governments. Their apprehension has been given credibility by the history of use of fraudulent identification papers and qualifications within the industry.

Forgery of Certificates of Competency and equivalent endorsements has long been a problem. As nations pump investment into keeping undesirables out, it would seem that a response by the maritime industry in rooting out documentary fraud is desperately required and also inevitable. This has led both the ILO and IMO to turn their attention to the topic of seafarer identification.

Provisions in the ILO's 1958 Convention No 108 (ILO 108) created an internationally-recognised identity document for crew travelling aboard seafaring vessels entering another country's designated seaport(s), known as the Seafarer's Identity Document (SID). Most crew members refer to the SID as seaman's books and they contain only records of the holder's career certification and experience.

The SID does not replace a crew member's passport and cannot be used to enter another country if arriving by air or by overland routes. It does, however, replace the requirement to present an entry, work or transit visa for those countries that have ratified ILO 108, provided that the crew member can evidence employment on a ship that is arriving at an ILO member state designated international seaport.

Under ILO 108 provisions, most ILO member states will grant qualified crew members shore leave of up to 30 consecutive days in a single stay without requiring a national entry or work visa. The period of visa-waiver is determined by each member state's national immigration laws and is applied on a case-by-case basis for each crew member.

If a vessel is transiting through the national waters of an ILO member state, the country of transit may waive the need for crew members holding valid SIDs recognised by that country to obtain transit visas.

In June 2003, ILO 108 was revised by the adoption of ILO 185, which includes the use of biometric identifiers. The ILO meeting finalised international standards for a new seafarer card that would provide a reliable, positively verifiable and internationally acceptable identification document. These standards were intended to facilitate shore leave, transit to and from ships and repatriation, and make it more straightforward to establish a seafarer's identity and qualification credentials.

Requirements under ILO 185

SIDs can only be issued by the crew member's country of nationality or country of legal, permanent residence. (Under ILO 108, SIDs can be issued by the crew member's country of nationality, country of the flag vessel or by the country of the crew member's employer)

SIDs must be machine-readable cards that contain the required biometric information of the crew member, similar to that of a new biometric passport

Each member state must implement minimum ILO requirements and recommended procedures for issue of SIDs and ensure crew members observe compliance with both ILO requirements and the host country's laws and regulations

Once a member state ratifies the new ILO 185 standards, all SIDs issued in accordance with ILO 108 will become invalid and new SID cards are to be issued by the seafarer's country of nationality or legal permanent residence. The cards will eventually replace the ILO 108 versions and are intended to reduce destination country entry visa requirements

One issue which has emerged is that a number of ILO member states enforce entry restrictions for certain nationalities. These states are unable to ratify ILO 185 until their national immigration laws change.

Particulars about the holder included in the SID are restricted to:

- Full name (first and last names where applicable)
- Sex
- Date and place of birth
- Nationality
- Any special physical characteristics that may assist identification
- Digital or original photograph
- Signature

In addition, a template or other representation of a biometric of the holder is required to be included.

This has created a problem as many ILO member states are finding it expensive and difficult to produce biometric identity documents and to install new machine-readable equipment at multiple ports of entry. This has greatly slowed the passage of ILO 185 regulations. Only 18 countries, representing 10% of the global seafarer supply, have ratified ILO 185.

Biometrics uses science and technology to measure and analyse biological data, such as fingerprints, eye retinas and irises, voice patterns, facial patterns and hand measurements, for authentication purposes.

Preconditions for the requirement for biometric data to be used on cards issued under ILO 185 include:

- Capture of data without any invasion of privacy, discomfort, health risks or offence against dignity
- Visibility on the document and protection ensuring it is not possible to reconstitute it from the template or other representation
- Equipment needed for provision and verification must be user-friendly and generally accessible to governments at low cost
- Equipment for verification can be conveniently and reliably operated in ports and in other places, including onboard ship
- Systems must provide uniform and reliable results
- Seafarers must have convenient access to machines enabling them to inspect any data concerning them that is not eye-readable

The first move towards using such technology was pioneered by the Liberian International Ship and Corporate Registry (LISCR) and its development of biometric identification cards for seafarers. However, efforts appear to have slowed as there have been issues of cost and reading equipment.

The roll-out has seen high profile complaints that onboard inspections of crew docking in US ports have had to take place without electronic tools, such as fingerprint scanners, to verify seafarer identity.

A US Government Accountability Office report stated that CBP field officials wanted a portable device, such as a fingerprint reader, but that such hand-held biometric devices were "several years away from being available".

It seems that in many countries the realities of processing biometric data have not kept step with the hope.

While seafarers are working with SID, various schemes are in place within particular countries for workers in ports and the maritime infrastructure. The US has taken a lead internally and MTSA mandated use of a transportation worker's ID to include biometric identifiers and appropriate background checks.

This scheme led to creation of the Transportation Worker Identification Credential (TWIC) scheme with the aim of ensuring individuals who pose a threat do not gain "unescorted access to secure areas" within the US maritime transportation system.

TWICs are tamper-resistant biometric credentials issued to workers who require unescorted access to secure areas of ports, vessels and outer continental shelf facilities, and to all credentialed merchant mariners.

Over 1 million workers including longshoremen, truckers, port employees and others are required to obtain a TWIC, through the scheme administered by the Transportation Security Administration (TSA) and USCG.

To obtain a TWIC, an individual must provide biographic and biometric information such as fingerprints, sit for a digital photograph and successfully pass a security threat assessment conducted by TSA. Pre-enrolment is recommended as it saves time for the applicant who provides biographical information and makes an appointment for enrolment in person.

The TWIC scheme has not been without problems and a range of issues have emerged, relating to issue, checking and cost. In fact many dub the scheme a very expensive failure, with cards that break, a lack of card readers and convicted felons being afforded the ability to move sensitive cargoes into restricted areas.

A number of other countries have national schemes in place, including Australia with its Maritime Security Identification Card. This is a nationally consistent identification card that is issued to identify a person who has been the subject of a background check. It shows that the holder needs to work unescorted or unmonitored in a maritime security zone and has met the minimum security requirements.

In many countries the identification of workers is the responsibility of the port and the checks and controls are administered internally.

Increased workload

Legislation, rules and guidelines often bring increased workload. While maritime security is an accepted and normal part of shipboard duties there are still implications from the extra work it can bring.

From the outset the ISPS Code was meant to increase security, not work load. The explicit guidance was that safe manning levels did not take into account any extra security duties.

Unfortunately for many the truth appears to be somewhat different and this can have a detrimental effect on not just security but also safety.

This issue is addressed within the MLC. In referring to manning levels, this states that seafarers shall work on board ships with sufficient personnel for the safe, efficient and secure operation of the ship.

Regulation 2.7 (manning levels) explains: "Each member shall require that all ships that fly its flag have a sufficient number of seafarers employed on board to ensure that ships are operated safely, efficiently and with due regard to security under all conditions, taking into account concerns about seafarer fatigue and the particular nature and conditions of the voyage."

In addition, Standard A2.7 (manning levels) states: "Every ship shall be manned by a crew that is adequate, in terms of size and qualifications, to ensure the safety and security of the ship and its personnel under all operating conditions, in accordance with the minimum safe manning document or an equivalent issued by the competent authority, and to comply with the MLC standards."

Unfamiliar roles

With smaller crew complements there is a need for people to take on additional duties to ensure that the requirements of the SSP can be met.

This means that there are often occasions when crew members from different departments have to work in unfamiliar areas of the vessel or work with equipment they are not familiar with.

What may be second nature for an experienced deck crew or a veteran engineer may not be for someone unused to working on deck, or aloft or in the confines of the machinery spaces. Where crews have to multi-task it is imperative that a risk assessment that reflects this is followed, and that personnel are fully familiarised with the tasks and the means of safe, effective completion.

Violence against seafarers

With the rising tide of piracy has come a trend for hostage-taking and in turn this has seen a despicable increase in the levels of violence against seafarers.

While the shipping industry can implement measures to better protect its people, cargoes and vessels, the plight of seafarers in captivity, or those still wrestling with the aftermath of having been held, should not be ignored.

Violence comes in many forms and all too often seafarers experience the full gamut – from physical beatings, being burned, electrocuted and frozen, through to psychological torture, such as the threat of death.

Working hard to implement the requirements of the ISPS Code is one thing but real action is needed at an international level. Government intervention is needed to fix the ills of failed states and to ease the suffering of seafarers. Until this intervention arrives we can only do our best. We have a moral obligation to protect ourselves but these efforts often appear ineffective in the face of the violent onslaught shipping is facing off the coast of Somalia, in the Gulf of Aden and across the Indian Ocean.

Command and control

With the use of armed guards increasing (see Chapter 9), there are issues facing seafarers, particularly the Master. The question of who is in charge of the ship remains.

Lawyers believe that if armed guards are onboard a fundamental question arises as to who authorises the use of force. With the launch of a standard maritime security contract (BIMCO's GUARDCON) some of the issues have been eased, especially for ship operators that have never employed the services of private armed forces for protection. Use of the contract is recommended. However, there are still security companies that will seek to insert clauses that appear to infer that the Master may not have overall control or make the final decision on whether weapons will be deployed and used. This is both highly contentious and concerning.

Where such clauses exist it appears that 'operational' decisions may rest with the security team, and that the Master only need be consulted 'if there is time'. The justification is that, if faced with a lethal threat, the right to self-defence outweighs Masters' overall responsibility for their crew and the environment. In other words, the Master may not have full control of a key area of the vessel's security, something which impacts directly on the safety of the crew and the vessel.

Armed force on a vessel must be in place for the safety of the crew and the protection of the environment and yet, by employing armed guards, owners may be forcing Masters to give up that discretion in breach of SOLAS regulations. This message is reinforced in the ISPS Code which states: 'At all times the Master of a ship has the ultimate responsibility for the safety and security of the ship.'

Such issues and questions may seem remote from everyday shipboard operations, yet in pirate high risk areas the question becomes very real. Speaking of the *Maersk Alabama* case in 2009, the vessel's then Master, Captain Richard Phillips said: "I am not comfortable giving command authority to others. In the heat of an attack, there can be only one final decision-maker." His comments seem to support the belief that Masters will not be comfortable giving up any of their overall authority on board. Owners, charterers and others should therefore give serious thought as to how they would deal with the issue of authority on board the vessel when considering employing armed guards.

The IMO has sought to inject some clarity as it addressed command and control of the onboard security team, including relationship with the Master in the interim guidelines on privately contracted armed security personnel (see Chapter 9).

Chapter 7
Security planning

KEY ADVICE

- Understanding the risk management approach
- Assessing the design and development of a security system
- Developing effective management of security procedures
- Understanding barriers to vigilance

The aim of security is to protect assets from identified threats through the employment of cost-effective measures. On ships, it does not stop with the consideration of cost but must also take into account the human resources that can be effectively utilised.

Out at sea, the security responses are limited by the number of people available. Efforts to comply with legislation and keep the vessel secure must be based on a realistic assessment of the constraints of crew, ship and equipment.

The most basic requirement of the ISPS Code is the production of an SSP. Certain steps must be taken before this is developed and after the plan is in operation.

To view the security of a vessel objectively and effectively and then translate these observations into a functioning and effective plan and onboard regime, a risk management approach to security has to be introduced. Formal risk management involves three basic tasks: identifying, assessing and prioritising the risks facing the people, vessel and the company or business.

Risk management

One of the primary drivers behind the ISPS Code was to develop an approach to maritime security which mirrored the risk management processes which exist in shipping. This view of risk as something which can be managed in a systematic manner is key to the creation of a maritime security regime onboard ship and supported ashore.

Key to such a risk management approach is the identification, assessment, and prioritisation of risks followed by coordinated and economical application of resources to minimise, monitor, and control the probability and/or impact of unfortunate events.

Risk is defined in ISO 31000 (Risk management – Principles and guidelines) as the effect of uncertainty on objectives, whether positive or negative. Safe to say, a terrorist attack or pirate raid would most definitely fall into the 'unfortunate events' category and so methods to manage the threats which conform to the requirements of the ISPS Code need to be created.

The strategies to manage risk in this maritime security setting include avoiding the risk, reducing the negative effect or probability of the risk.

A 'CEDI' approach is a good way to analyse the security in place on a vessel and to assess any vulnerabilities and threats. This involves:

- Consideration
- Evaluation
- Determination
- Implementation

Consideration

A wide view must be taken and any threats likely to affect the security of the vessel anticipated. Assessment of threat and security risk is an continuing process and should be a response to intelligence, changes in trading patterns and the evolving threat profile of the vessel, crew, flag state and the vessel's activities.

It is imperative that the CSO and SSO continually monitor and respond to any new threats that the vessel may face.

Evaluation

Once a comparison of risks has been conducted, a proper allocation of security resources can be made. The standard approach of giving each risk a qualitative rating, depending on a combination of its likelihood and impact, is useful.

The threats identified earlier in the process can then be transposed onto the specific make-up and construction of the vessel, taking into account any security equipment and systems or procedures already in existence. For example, assessment can be made of a vessel's susceptibility to attack, such as having a low freeboard or operating at a slow speed.

Any perceived weaknesses in infrastructure or procedures, such as a small crew complement or generic procedures that do not take the vessel, crew or equipment into account, must also be examined.

Determination

Of mitigating strategies – solutions and measures to eliminate or reduce the threat or to minimise its consequences – can then be decided on. When the risk posed by certain threats is low, the decision may be to simply accept the risk. This does not mean it can be ignored completely, rather that it should be monitored for change and may need to be guarded against later.

Implementation

Of protective measures. When a set of threats has been generated and decisions have been made on the level of risk posed by them, a set of protective measures to guard the crew, environment, vessel, company and cargo must be developed. These can take many forms and should provide the most effective and suitable means of guarding the appropriate assets.

Security system design

Effective security depends on the design and development of the security system. It is about making the elements (equipment and resources) work in harmony together to keep the vessel or area secure.

CCTV cameras dazzled by security lights are an obvious waste of both resources. Poorly placed alarm sensors that are obscured by parts of the superstructure cannot provide the protection required and lights that cause excessive areas of shadow serve to obscure threats rather than detect them.

When placing equipment onboard, or allocating resources, the basic security design principles are:

- Strongest barrier closest to target
- Earliest warning furthest from target
- Mixture of measures to suit operations
- Safety considerations override security requirements

In designing a system to protect a vessel to the standards required by the ISPS Code, the following have to be taken into account:

Access to the vessel

Both officially designated points and places where persons may try to gain access must be considered. Mooring ropes and fairleads, anchor chains, rudder housings and pilot boarding areas are popular and tempting unauthorised access points.

Access within the vessel

Ease of movement for intruders once access has been gained to the accommodation and machinery spaces must be assessed. Identifying freedom of movement within the vessel will lead to addressing ease of access to certain areas where security is more critical.

Security of restricted areas

As part of the security planning process areas that are to be restricted must be identified and protected accordingly. An assessment should be made of whether these restricted areas being protected adequately and in accordance with the SSP.

Consideration must also be given to sensitive areas, vulnerable areas, infrastructure and procedures in order to secure the vessel's key operations

Security of non-restricted areas

While not such a priority, these areas must still be afforded some degree of protection. Freedom of access to these areas could impinge on the security of restricted areas.

Cargo handling

Whatever the vessel type, movement of cargo onto and off the ship poses some form of security risk. To minimise the risk, systems must be in place to ensure cargo is legitimate and does not pose an undue security risk. Even legitimate cargo has associated dangers, so all cargo must be dealt with a safe and secure way.

Handling of ship's stores

Stores are another area of vulnerability as they provide a fast and easy way of placing items onboard that should not be loaded. Systems in place must ensure that stores are legitimate, have not been tampered with and are securely stowed upon loading.

Handling of unaccompanied baggage

Except for passenger ships, the concept of unaccompanied baggage is fairly rare but each vessel must still have procedures in place. Is it allowed onboard? How can its authenticity be checked? What percentage is to be screened or searched?

All these issues matters need to be addressed by the CSO and SSO and within the SSP. Large offshore vessels, for example, will often have groups of technicians, divers, surveyors and company representatives coming onboard. This poses a risk of unaccompanied baggage and systems are required to deal with this.

Security levels

In considering and evaluating these vulnerable points and allocating security responses, all security levels must be covered. The appropriate frequency and intensity of security measures and their effectiveness must be assessed whether the vessel is at Security Level 1, 2 or 3.

Security measures

The most common maritime security measures involve a specific or combined use of four basic components: physical barriers; electronic systems; security management procedures; response by shipboard personnel

Physical barriers take the form of obstacles that serve to frustrate trivial attackers and delay serious ones. They include means to delay or deny access to the vessel or restricted areas and to control movement around the vessel

The main purpose of physical security is to deter attackers by persuading them that the likely costs of attack exceed the value of making it. These measures can be as simple as a locked door or as elaborate as multiple layers of electronic sensors, locks and alarms.

Provision of physical barriers allows security to be layered as the vessel is compartmentalised into areas that can be readily controlled. It allows provision of defence in depth as attackers are forced to move from one security measure into another. Physical barriers would include razor wire, locked doors and bars on ports and windows.

Electronic systems are likely to account for a large part of the investment in maritime security hardware. The primary role for such equipment is providing early warning and detection of attack. This can be by sight or sound and by monitoring movement around a vessel – of both friend and foe.

Common equipment includes:

- CCTV. Provides early warning of intrusion and also be used as evidence after a security breach
- Electronic access control. Allows personnel to move freely while acting as part of physical barrier defence to lock out attackers
- Intruder detection systems (IDS). Detect presence in unattended areas. Often use very basic passive infrared sensors similar to those used in home security systems

Chapter 9 of this publication gives more details of security equipment available.

Security management procedures are a vital tool in securing a vessel, as any piece of security equipment is only as effective as the system within which it works. Increasingly, the maritime industry has grown accustomed to working within management systems and security sits ever more comfortably alongside the provisions already laid down within a vessel's SMS.

Effective security management procedures ensure that attacks are deterred and prevented; potential and actual security breaches are reported and monitored; and any attacks are responded to. Once the security management process is started it is necessary to assess the effectiveness of the measures to counter any threats to the vessel.

Countermeasures must include:

- Good procedures. A strong security management system
- Consistency. Rules that apply at all times, to all personnel

- Unpredictability. Keep attackers guessing by applying the rules consistently but making the interpretation unpredictable
- Vigilance. All senses used and harnessed with an awareness of the vessel and the threats that may face it

Response by shipboard personnel. A vessel may have the best equipment and work under the most effective security management systems but all this counts for nothing without the involvement of adequately trained, motivated and supported shipboard personnel.

Personnel play a pivotal role in a swift and effective security response in protecting the vessel and mitigating the effects of any breaches of security that do occur. Shipboard personnel should:

- Carry out specific security duties
- Be vigilant
- Monitor the security of the vessel
- Report incidents
- Collect evidence
- Liaise with shore-side personnel (CSO, PFSO, port state officials, Customs, immigration, law enforcement)
- Respond to security threats and incidents when necessary and as required by the SSP

Key to the response of personnel and the level of vigilance displayed onboard the vessel is an awareness of the importance of security. The awareness necessary to maintain a secure and vigilant vessel takes a number of different forms, but at all levels it requires the Master, SSO, officers and crew to have certain levels of knowledge and training, such as who may threaten security and the nature and geographic location of threats.

Personnel should have a general awareness of the threats facing them but should also be aware of specific threats based on current intelligence and historical evidence. The crew and officers of most vessels are extremely aware of the threat posed by, say, pirates off the coast of Somalia and similar levels of awareness should be fostered and applied equally to all areas.

It is also important that personnel understand the vulnerabilities of the vessel, including its physical structure and construction, operational considerations and personnel themselves. They need to be confident in identifying threats to the vessel and when and how to report such threats.

Barriers to vigilance

A concern for any security culture is that there are many barriers to vigilance, and the shipping industry has historically been beset by a number of these.

Tiredness, overwork and fatigue are all major barriers to vigilance. While all onboard work is under the auspices of the STCW Convention hours of rest rules, however, many believe the minimum manning standards applicable on vessels do not take into account the extra work generated by the requirements of the ISPS Code.

Security has now been explicitly mentioned and the Manila amendments to STCW take this into account when outlining the rest hours for watchkeeping personnel. Officers who are assigned duty as officer in charge of a watch, or ratings forming part of a watch, and personnel whose duties involve designated safety, prevention of pollution and security duties, should have not less than 10 hours of rest in any 24-hour period and 77 hours in any seven-day period.

The hours of rest may be divided into no more than two periods, one of which shall be at least six hours in length, and the intervals between consecutive periods of rest should not exceed 14 hours.

It is vital that the SSO closely monitors the performance of personnel who have security duties to ensure they are adequately rested and able to perform to the levels necessary.

It is recognised that ships are busy and that personnel may feel they do not have the time to strictly follow security procedures or remain vigilant. It is tempting to leave doors unlocked or to allow visitors to move freely about the vessel. Lack of time is no excuse, however, and the Master, CSO and SSO must stress that priority must be afforded to security.

It is clear that unless personnel fully appreciate the threat facing them there is little chance of them being willing or able to adopt security as an important part of shipboard life and operations. A lack of training, knowledge and skills is a serious barrier to progress and it is the job of the Master, CSO and SSO to identify those who are lacking the necessary skills. It will then be necessary to ensure that the crew members understand what is expected of them and also the reasons for undertaking their tasks.

A lack of training can lead to wrong response, or no response at all. Until all crew and officers are fully conversant with all the provisions within the SSP no true security culture can exist.

Complacency does on occasion inevitably creep into many shipboard operations and security is no different. It is the job of the Master, CSO and SSO to ensure that complacency is guarded against and that all personnel who have security responsibilities remain alert and focused.

With so many tasks to perform, and so many other calls on shipboard resources, crew members can be distracted from important tasks. It is imperative that security is given such a high profile and prioritised role within shipboard operations that people concentrate on securing the vessel.

The role of the Master, CSO and SSO in safeguarding and fostering awareness and vigilance has been highlighted. This burden has been placed on these ranks by the ISPS Code and they have to constantly ensure that security is taken seriously and that all personnel are alert to the threats and the correct response.

The positions of Master, CSO and SSO are pivotal in making a vessel secure. Without a united and concerted effort to embrace the contents of the SSP and make them second nature to all onboard, the vessel may comply on paper but in reality will be no more secure than before the ISPS Code.

Beating the barriers to vigilance

A number of simple steps can be introduced to overcome the problems associated with lapses in concentration and vigilance, and to keep complacency at bay.

Foremost of these would be measures which ensure personnel are well versed in what is expected of them. Training, drills and exercises are key to this, and will allow officers to appreciate where problems may potentially be found in the security regime,

It is also important to understand the effect of shipboard morale on security. While even the most dissatisfied crew members may still react to keep themselves safe, the same cannot often be said of security.

Slack, slovenly behaviour all too often translates into a failed security regime. Through engagement, encouragement and inclusion all can play a pivotal role in security. However, in order to embrace security and to break down the barriers to vigilance people need to be resourced, supported and appreciated,

Security management may sound complicated at times, but it does require dedication, commitment and leadership in order for the basics to succeed.

Chapter 8

Basic shipboard security procedures

KEY ADVICE

- Understanding the basic approaches to security
- Developing a regime to monitor and control access
- Developing effective search procedures
- Developing a response to bomb threats and incidents

This chapter gives an overview of some of the most common security practices that may constitute part of any maritime security regime. This is intended as guidance only and should not be considered to take precedence over the exact security requirements and procedures laid down within the vessel's own SSP or the orders given by the Master, CSO or SSO.

For further information on additional security procedures necessary in transiting waters where pirates are known to be active see The Nautical Institute *Piracy Handbook*. For further information on searching for stowaways and criminal activities see the *Stowaway Handbook* and *Crime at Sea Handbook*.

Controlling access

The ISPS Code requires:

- Prevention of unauthorised persons gaining access
- Prevention of unauthorised loading or discharge of goods and cargo
- Prevention of the introduction of unauthorised weapons, incendiary devices, dangerous and illegal substances or explosives
- Control of movement on, off and around the vessel
- Prevention of stowaways
- Deterrence of attempted crime and terrorism
- Coming onboard: knowledge of who, what and when
- Leaving the vessel: knowledge of who, what and when

All onboard need to know what to do to control access and when and how to do it. There must be procedures covering embarkation and disembarkation and communication (internal and ship-to-shore) and for logging information.

It is also important to monitor deck areas, areas surrounding the ship and restricted areas onboard. Handling of cargo and ship's stores has an effect on security and if something goes wrong there needs to be a reporting and communication system in place.

Once rules have been drawn up they should be applied with the normal common sense of good seamanship to make the vessel secure.

The gangway is the easiest and most obvious point of access to a vessel when it is moored or at anchor. It is vital the gangway watch is given clear boarding procedures and instructions on when to call for assistance.

Control and monitoring

Potential means of access

- Access ladders
- Access gangways
- Access ramps
- Access doors, side scuttles, windows and ports
- Mooring lines and anchor chains
- Cranes and hoisting gear: when searching, one crew member should be posted outside the crane as another searches inside to ensure that unauthorised boarders cannot exit the crane unseen and escape
- Rudder housings

Restricted areas

- Navigation bridge
- Machinery spaces and control spaces
- Security equipment control spaces
- Ventilation and air conditioning systems and spaces
- Access to potable water tanks, pumps and controls
- Other ship-specific areas, as in the SSP

Restricted property and equipment

- Dangerous goods and hazardous substances
- Cargo pumps
- Cargo spaces
- Ship's stores and essential maintenance equipment
- Navigation and communications equipment
- Medical equipment and stores

Vulnerable areas may include any key areas identified in the SSP, but not mentioned above, and areas where unauthorised access could cause harm to people, vessel, equipment or cargo.

Procedures must be in place to ensure that the gangway is never left unattended, even if the gangway watch is obliged to take on additional responsibilities. Some form of contingency planning should be in place to ensure that replacement personnel are available.

Being secure is a permanent state. Although the level of threat can go up and down, it is never below Security Level 1. Security must always be taken seriously and the instructions contained in the SSP followed.

Some vessels with apparently excellent daytime gangway security let down their guard after dark. Coverage and vigilance over the whole 24 hours must be ensured.

Any security instructions need to make allowances for differing operations and it is important that personnel are aware of the implications for security that are posed by each state:

- At sea – full away, manoeuvering or pilotage
- Moored in port – working cargo and silent periods
- At anchor
- Alongside buoy moorings
- In dynamic positioning mode
- Not under command
- Restricted in ability to manoeuvre
- In drydock
- Ship-to-ship transfer
- Search and rescue
- Emergencies
- Conducting exercises and drills

It is also vital to assess the effect of the tide. For example, a vessel with a low freeboard may become more susceptible to unauthorised entry when the tide drops to a certain level. It is important that the OOW, and anyone else with security duties, remain aware of the implications of such changes.

The state of a vessel can change throughout operations and the threats posed can also change.

While the Master has overall responsibility for the safety and security of the crew, ship and cargo and the SSO is responsible for implementing, maintaining and supervising all security procedures, training, drills, exercises and personnel assigned security duties onboard under the overall authority of the Master, the OOW may be responsible for:

- Supervising security patrols and gangway watch
- Assisting gangway watch as required
- Processing visitors

Personnel with security duties should do as instructed at all times and all other personnel as a minimum must:

- Maintain security vigilance
- Challenge and question any unescorted person on board who is not a crew member
- Assist in the performance of vessel searches

- Report deficiencies such as broken or missing locks and lights
- Ask questions if they are unsure

Granting and denying access

The Master or SSO should instruct security watches with details of who is allowed access and what they need to provide to satisfy security demands.

Such persons are likely to include:

- Shipboard personnel and staff
- Passengers
- Officials (immigration, port state, Customs, law enforcement, coastguard, port health)
- Company personnel (CSO, superintendents, office staff)
- Operational visitors
- Bona fide visitors
- Supernumeraries
- Contractors and surveyors
- Agents
- Port officials (PFSO, terminal managers, stevedores)

In addition to having strict rules of who may be allowed onboard, such people must be able to prove beyond doubt that they are who they claim to be. For example, there have been reports of stowaways gaining access to vessels by masquerading as stevedores and it is important to remain alert to the threat posed by people using faked credentials to gain access.

The SSP will list the criteria for entry to the vessel and these may be supplemented with a list of expected visitors who have arranged to visit the vessel at the particular port or anchorage.

In monitoring and controlling access to the vessel it is best to err on the side of caution. It is far better to delay a legitimate visitor and to ask for clarification of ID than it is to allow access to someone who should not be onboard.

In the event that someone turns abusive or violent the watchperson needs to call for immediate assistance from the SSO or OOW, who will hopefully be able to calm the situation and act as necessary.

A record should be kept and, if deemed necessary, a report should be forwarded to the PFSO. The port should have procedures in place to deal with people who abuse or threaten ship personnel.

If someone has been denied access it is important to monitor their progress off the vessel and the SSP should contain advice for escorting them from the vessel safely.

Options for access control and monitoring

Access can be controlled in four ways – physical, electronic, human and procedural – and a layered mix of these usually works best.

Physical barriers, such as gangway gates or barriers, seals, doors with locks and keys, signage and fences are the most basic and common-sense measures to deter, slow or stop unauthorised access onto or around the vessel.

Their use is fairly straightforward and they should be positioned to work in conjunction with the other layers of security in place. They can also be used to push visitors into the next line of defence.

Although such equipment is basic it still requires planning, foresight and training to position and use it in the most effective way.

Locks for instance, need to be used properly. There are many ships that simply leave padlocks hanging down or do not close doors. This needs to be addressed and all personnel with security duties should familiarise themselves with the measures in place and keep a check that all are used correctly.

Monitoring can be achieved through electronic and human means and again a mixed approach is likely to bring the best results.

Electronic systems include access control systems, CCTV, automated intruder detection (AID) and alarm systems and lighting. Advanced electronic systems can boost any security regime but, as with physical measures, they need to be used correctly.

Electronic access control and alarm systems need to be armed and operational. The investment in such equipment can be significant and all personnel should be familiar with its operation and any weaknesses.

CCTV systems can greatly increase the capability of personnel to monitor and protect large areas. However, it is important that cameras are sited correctly, that they work in harmony with other security measures (particularly lighting) and are monitored effectively.

Lighting can be a very strong deterrent to boarders but again must be used and fitted correctly. Avoid creating areas of shadow that can provide boarders with places to hide. Also avoid blinding or dazzling security personnel and CCTV systems.

Over-reliance on any system can be detrimental and should be guarded against. All means available should be used to monitor security and cross-referencing of systems should be routine.

When used, AID devices should activate an audible and/or visual alarm at a location that is continuously attended or monitored.

Human control and monitoring is usually organised into surveillance, patrolling and gangway, overside and deck watch. Shipboard personnel are vital to security, and they need to be:

- Fully briefed
- Knowledgeable about their instructions
- Confident
- Trained and practiced
- Supported by their seniors
- Familiar with security measures in place

The shipboard security regime is only as good as the people working within it. If personnel are confident, understand their roles and responsibilities and appreciate how important they are, then the security will reflect this.

It is important that those charged with controlling access to the vessel understand they are in the frontline of the security efforts and need to do everything possible to ensure they are up to this challenge.

Having people at the access point who look, sound and act with a reassuring confidence can have a major effect on the security of the vessel. Such people deter unauthorised boarders (they will simply move on to the next vessel) and also act as a catalyst for security improvement around the whole vessel.

Security is no different from any other shipboard activity – people need to be trained, skilled, enthusiastic and positive in order to achieve.

Procedures for access control should lay down clear rules for checking of people, what ID is acceptable, when to deny access and when to call the SSO or OOW. Such procedures will harness the physical, electronic and human elements of security and demonstrate that the vessel is doing as required by the ISPS Code. They will also ensure that security assets are used properly and to their best effect.

It is also important to document what was done so that procedures feed back into the vital record-keeping requirements for the vessel.

Main access point

The SSP should designate a proper means of access. This is usually a gangway or accommodation ladder and, whatever the security level in force, should be the proper means of access to the vessel and the focal point of access control measures.

If access is not properly controlled, stowaways will take the easiest option to try and sneak on board. That could well be the main access point if security is lax.

The proper means of access benefits from being set up as a formal reception area. There should be clear external signs directing all visitors.

An entrance doorway should be designated by the SSP as the main entrance for reception of visitors. This should be clearly marked and situated so that the watch person is the first point of contact for the visitor. Ideally there will be some protection from the weather and an area for the watch person to process visitors.

Ideally this should be a lockable door that will only be opened when the watch person has deemed that access is permissible. It may be advisable for there to be an alarm activation point or permanent means of communication installed here.

All other doors should carry signs stating: No admittance to unauthorised personnel.

Many ships alternate gangways depending on the port being visited, so it is advisable to replicate the reception areas on the port and starboard access points. On vessels using ramps, or alternative arrangements, the same consideration should be given to safety, control and comfort of personnel.

The SSO should use his judgment in setting up a security reception area which will work within the ship's specific layout.

The reception area should be clean and safe and as personnel will be performing some basic safety and housekeeping checks alongside their security duties, such guidance may be contained within the vessel's SMS. This will include checking:

- Gangway is properly lashed and secure
- Lighting
- Safe for use
- Persons boarding
- Approaches to the vessel
- Unauthorised boarding
- Security signs in place

If anything happens, security personnel need to respond correctly, whether by reporting or requesting assistance. Security watch personnel should know the order in which to call for assistance and the circumstances under which to initiate an alarm. They should have no doubt or confusion and should be very clear on the benefits of prompt and decisive action.

The gangway watch reports to the SSO or the OOW and is responsible for deterring unauthorised entry and detecting unauthorised persons.

The SCAR approach

1 Stop   **2 Check**   **3 Act (allow or deny access)**   **4 Record**

On entry:

- Stop all persons attempting to gain access
- Check and authorise – Who are they visiting? Are they expected? Are they listed? ID – check photos, validity, issuing authority
- Deny entry to unauthorised visitors
- Issue visitor's pass to legitimate visitors, as in the SSP
- Arrange escort as required
- Record details

On exit:

- Retrieve visitor's pass
- Record time of leaving
- Ensure persons actually depart

A visitor log should be maintained at the gangway. Systematic control and logging of those who come onboard provides focus to the whole security regime and supports the efforts to protect against unauthorised boarders.

Minimum details recorded should include:

- Name
- Company
- ID seen and deemed acceptable
- Person visited
- Date and time of boarding
- Date and time of leaving
- Visitor badge number issued
- Comments (if necessary)

Extra details may be laid down within the SSP.

The importance of the visitor log should be stressed to all personnel and the fact that it should never, under any circumstance, be falsified.

The log book needs to be kept neat, legible and up-to-date. Knowing that all visitors have left the vessel closes down the opportunity for stowaways to try and gain "official" access, hoping to remain onboard once the vessel sails.

Access control at Security Levels 1, 2 and 3

At Security Level 1

- Check the identity of all persons seeking to board the ship and confirm point of contact onboard
- In liaison with the port facility, establish secure areas for inspecting and searching people, baggage (including carry-on items) and personal effects
- Segregation of checked persons and their personal effects from unchecked persons and their personal effects
- Control of embarkation and disembarkation
- Identification of access points that should be secured or monitored to prevent unauthorised access
- Secure access to unattended spaces that adjoin areas with visitor access
- Provision of security briefings to all ship personnel on possible threats, reporting and the need for vigilance
- Searches of those boarding as in the SSP at Level 1

At Security Level 2

As at Level 1, plus extra security measures to ensure higher vigilance and tighter access control and monitoring.

- Increased frequency of patrols around deck areas during night-time hours to deter unauthorised access
- If necessary, limit the number of access points to the ship, identify those to be closed and the means of adequately securing them
- Where possible deter or prevent waterside access to the ship
- Encourage the PFSO to establish a restricted area on the shore-side of the ship, in close cooperation with the port facility
- Increase frequency and detail of searches of people and personal effects
- Escort visitors while on board
- Provide additional specific security briefings to all ship personnel
- Full or partial search of the ship
- Search those boarding as in the SSP at Level 2

continued ...

At Security Level 3

As at Levels 1 and 2, plus compliance with instructions issued by those responding to the security incident or threat.

- Additional resources to guard access control at the single, controlled access point
- Only those responding to the security incident or threat allowed access
- More personnel readied to respond on board
- Suspension of embarkation or disembarkation
- If instructed, suspension of cargo-handling operations, deliveries etc.
- Steps prepared for evacuation
- Steps prepared for any necessary movement of the ship when instructed
- Preparation for a full or partial search of the ship if instructed
- Unless instructed otherwise, provision of a briefing to personnel informing them of the security status
- Searches of those boarding as in the SSP at Level 3, or by instruction from authorised parties

The issue of official security levels is difficult to manage as many ports, even those with security problems, may still be operating at Security Level 1. That can cause serious problems for the vessel trying to react to the risk it is facing.

The Master, SSO and CSO need to make plans to enable the vessel's security to react effectively to the risk. This could be by boosting the main access control, making a visible presence around the vessel and tightly controlling and checking the perimeter of the vessel and vulnerable areas, such as rudder housings.

Monitoring security

The ISPS Code states that ship personnel should have the capability to monitor the ship itself, restricted areas on board and the areas surrounding it.

Minimum capabilities may include use of lighting, watchkeepers, security guards and deck watches including patrols and AID devices and surveillance equipment (as already described).

The SSP will outline the procedures and equipment needed at each security level. It will also outline the means of ensuring that monitoring equipment will be able to perform continually, including consideration of the possible effects of weather conditions or power disruptions.

Maintenance of sophisticated security equipment is important, and failure to properly install, maintain or repair can compromise the effectiveness of both the equipment and the vessel's security.

Monitoring at Security Levels 1, 2 and 3

At Security Level 1

The ISPS Code states that the SSP should establish the security measures to be applied, which may be a combination of lighting, watchkeepers, security guards or use of security and surveillance equipment, to allow ship's security personnel to observe the ship in general and barriers and restricted areas in particular.

The deck and access points should be illuminated during the hours of darkness and periods of low visibility while operating in port or at a port facility or anchorage when necessary.

At Security Level 2

Additional security measures in the SSP may include:

- Increased frequency and detail of security patrols
- Increased coverage and intensity of lighting or the use of security surveillance and equipment. This may involve coordination with the port facility to provide additional shore-side lighting
- Additional personnel as security lookouts
- Coordination with waterside boat patrols and foot or vehicle patrols on the shore-side when provided

At Security Level 3

At this stage the vessel will need to comply with instructions issued by those responding to the security incident or threat. The SSP should detail the security measures which could be taken by the ship, in close cooperation with those responding, and the port facility, including:

- All lighting to illuminate the ship vicinity to be switched on
- All onboard surveillance equipment capable of recording activities on or in the vicinity of the ship to be switched on
- Maximise surveillance equipment recording time
- Prepare for underwater hull inspection
- Initiate measures including slow revolution of the propellers, if practicable, to deter underwater access to the hull

Monitoring and controlling access to the vessel are the main keys to managing the stowaway threat. If attempted boarders are spotted and robust control measures are in place, the ship is a harder target. In problem ports, it is vital that sufficient resources are allocated to keep unauthorised boarders at bay.

Access control training, exercises and drills

Training can be done in a number of ways. For gangway watch and monitoring duties, often the best approach is simple role playing. Other crew members should take on a range of different roles – some should be granted access, others should be denied, and some should be troublesome visitors for whom a greater degree of response may be necessary.

Range of exercises

- Unauthorised boarder spotted trying to gain access
- Dealing with unruly persons attempting to use the entrance point
- Stowaway located onboard
- Several stowaways found
- Apprehending stowaways
- Violent response from stowaways
- Questioning techniques

Security provisions to control and monitor access, particularly to deter stowaways, should not compromise the safety of personnel or the vessel. At all times Masters have the ultimate responsibility for the safety and security of the ship and if, in their professional judgment, a conflict between any safety and security requirements arises they must remember that the safety of the ship is paramount.

The example has been given of a surveyor attending a vessel fitted with one stern-launched lifeboat. In an attempt to prevent stowaways, the lifeboat access door was secured with a substantial chain, fitted, in turn, with an equally substantial padlock.

The apparent intention was to unlock this before putting to sea but this was overlooked. An engineer wished to perform routine maintenance and testing on the lifeboat engine and was unable to gain access. The key was in the third mate's cabin, effectively rendering the ship's only lifeboat completely useless. Security does not take priority over safety.

Basics of shipboard searching

Different types of search exist and can be summed up in the categories of precautionary, deterrent or preventative.

Precautionary search

A precautionary search can be employed without any specific threat information and as a response to the general security risk or the perceived need for increased security measures. It can be instigated either randomly or as part of a general security procedure.

If the vessel is in a hotspot of stowaway activity a precautionary search should be undertaken – usually in the form of a pre-departure search. Unfortunately, because this is the most common type of search and as it takes place at a time of high activity on the vessel, there is the danger that shortcuts may be taken. The officer and crew charged with carrying out the search will probably have other, competing duties – they may be on their way to mooring stations, for instance.

It is vital that even in this busy period, the search is given the priority and emphasis it deserves. In high-risk ports, consideration should be given to anchoring in some convenient position outside the port and making a final stowaway search after the tugs and pilots depart.

Any stowaways found in this final search can then be discharged directly to the shore authorities, potentially minimising the costs that might otherwise be incurred if stowaways were to be discovered later. This is particularly important, as there are significant advantages to fixing the problem in the stowaway's port of embarkation.

Deterrent search

A deterrent search can be used to demonstrate visible security measures, with the aim of displaying an effective and working security regime. It can be instigated whenever the security threat warrants pre-emptive action.

Seeing physical security measures being carried out may deter those seeking to compromise the ship's security. Stowaways, terrorists or smugglers viewing the vessel and witnessing continuing searches may simply move on to the next, less security-aware vessel.

Preventative search

A preventative search is employed whenever a security threat is confirmed. There may be some strong information or intelligence with which to plan the search action. An example could be intelligence received from third-party experts who might give warning of local stowaways concealing themselves in a particular part of the ship. Such searches often employ dog teams.

Searches should be conducted based on the size and construction of the ship and the resources available. Some ships will have a limited number of people available to carry out the search and in this case it is important to prioritise the search within clearly defined limits and, on some occasions, disregard areas that do not require a search.

Searches can be carried out in three basic ways: by area, of the cargo and of persons (this will be covered in detail in The Nautical Institute's *Stowaway Handbook*).

Area searches include compartments and facilities that form part of, or are fixed to, the ship's structure, which are permanently onboard and integral to the vessel's operations. Ship's stores and storage areas are included.

Cargo searches cover all items being legally transported by the ship for legitimate business purposes, including vehicles on ro-ro vessels.

In accordance with the responsibilities of the Master, SSO and OOW described earlier, the OOW may be responsible for supervising:

- Search personnel
- Access control to the ship
- Search of visitors at access points

The responsibilities of personnel with security duties and the minimum requirements for all other personnel are detailed within the ISPS Code, and should be explicitly stated in the SSP.

Search plans should be available on all vessels and incorporated into the SSP. There are, however, a number of considerations common to planning all categories of search.

All onboard should be familiar with the areas of the vessel they may have responsibility for searching. The plans also need to be understood and familiar to all those charged with such duties.

Initial questions include:

- What Security Level is, or shall be considered to be, in force at the time the search is to be carried out? This will determine search criteria in accordance with ISPS
- What is the category of the search? Is it a precaution, a deterrent or preventative?
- Is the search an area or cargo search? In some cases it will be both
- Are there witnesses to question? Was something seen or heard or has something been found?

It is important to clearly define the scope of the search, the search limits and timeframe. The SSO should liaise with the CSO and port authorities in establishing the parameters of the search plan.

The search may apply only to certain areas or it may be a general search of the whole vessel. It may be a search of cargo taken onboard at the current port, for example. By defining the priority and the start point, resources will be used to the best advantage.

Planning the search

Knowing the object of the search influences the way the search is conducted, by whom and whether outside agencies will have to be notified or called in to assist. Both the object of the search and the area being searched can present a risk to the searcher. In the interests of safety, all potential hazards must be identified, prior to search if possible, and suitable plans put in place to deal with them.

Searching for people and searching of people may expose the search team to potential confrontation and they should be briefed and equipped to deal with this.

All searches will require the allocation of resources. Availability of manpower, the priority of the search and the nature of the threat will dictate how the search will be conducted.

People can work for long periods of time under normal conditions, but generally under more stressful conditions concentration can lapse and concentration can diminish rapidly. This should be borne in mind when applying manpower to search tasks and in setting the scope, limitations and timeframe of the search.

Equipment falls into two categories and should be allocated as required: items with which to carry out the search and items required for personal safety purposes – individual protective equipment (IPE).

If the Master or SSO feels the guidance in the SSP is inadequate, or does not reflect the capabilities of the personnel, manpower or vessel design, these concerns should be raised with the CSO at the earliest opportunity and corrective action taken.

Carrying out an area search

1 Establish the search team. Teams should be allocated well in advance

- Use trained personnel where possible
- Try to ensure they are available for the whole of the search operation
- Ideally they should be familiar with the area to be searched
- Consider using personnel who work in the area to be searched who have an intimate knowledge of it
- Teams should be made up of at least two persons
- Teams should be equipped as required. (A list of appropriate equipment is listed page 116)
- A search supervisor should be appointed

2 Establish the reporting chain and search control point

- Designate the search control point. The bridge is a logical location but may not be the most practical
- Decide who will control the search operation
- Decide how information will be passed up and down the chain of command
- Raise a search log

3 Create a search plan based on the SSP and the information available

- Define the scope of the search – where to look and what to look for
- Prioritise the areas for search according to the threat or information received
- Allocate teams to the areas and state their responsibilities clearly
- Describe how the search teams are to report their findings. Teams should report regularly, at least on completion of one search task before moving on to another
- Decide on actions to be taken by the teams on discovering stowaways. Knowing what to do next is vital
- Establish procedures for searching hazardous areas

continued …

4 Brief the search team

- Personnel designated to search should be thoroughly briefed on all the points given at 3, including any applicable safety information
- Explain to the search team the actions they should initiate if something of interest is found
- Split the briefing into two phases: a general briefing applicable to all searchers, including any background information and the object of the search, and individual briefings as applicable
- The search controller should take steps to ensure searchers understand the briefing and their own responsibilities

Searching an area can be broken down for ease of management and to ensure that the search carried out is thorough.

- External surfaces. All open areas above deck, including the hull down to the waterline
- Internal areas. All areas below deck, including enclosed areas, rooms and compartments

Search procedures are simple but require practice and a degree of patience. A search should be carried out in a methodical and logical fashion. Dividing an area into zones is one way to accomplish this; another way is to divide up the area by contents.

Searching an enclosed area, room or compartment using the division method involves dividing it up into logical sections or zones, eg the deck and everything on it; bulkheads and any openings; deck head and any openings.

Further sub-divide depending on the complexity and size of the area. For example, search a deck to specified points or bulkheads to waist height. Use existing fittings as templates, so search under all freestanding furniture or inside any integral fittings. Let the surroundings guide decisions on dividing the area.

Complete the search in a logical manner (eg side to side, front to back). Before starting the search, identify and report all items not usually found in the area and items that appear out of place or suspicious. If the search team members are not familiar with the area, find someone who is.

If two people are searching together, divide the area up and then if time allows get them to swap over and search each other's areas for thoroughness. It may be worthwhile to consider a non-permanent method of marking those areas that have been searched and subsequently confirmed as not being a security risk.

Once the search is complete, report the findings to the search supervisor or controller.

Dividing areas

This is a general guide to the areas to search. It is not exhaustive and common sense and knowledge of the problem areas of the specific vessel are essential tools of searching.

Using this guide, it should be possible to generate a more extensive and specific list for individual purposes.

Area search checklist

Accommodation

- Under bunks – on the deck or attached to the bunk frame
- Bedding – inside mattresses
- Behind drawers or in closets – all surfaces of the carcass. Check for false backs and bottoms
- Above the deckhead space and behind bulkhead panels or mouldings
- Ventilator grills and ducts
- Heater and air conditioning units
- Behind any protruding bulkheads and boxes

Galleys and mess areas

- Food bins and dry goods
- Among fresh vegetables and fruit sacks and bags
- On shelves behind tinned and packaged goods, bottles and cartons
- Inside galley units, fridges, freezers and extraction units
- Inside storage rooms and bonded lockers
- Dining areas – inside or under furniture and fittings

Showers and toilets

- Behind ventilator grills and ducts
- Behind panelling and access plates in the decks, bulkheads or deckheads
- Behind exposed and blocked-in piping

Engine rooms

- Machinery – shrouds, cofferdams, control boxes, sumps, pedestals and bilges
- Ventilation shafts, piping and ducts
- Inside tanks
- Under deck plating
- Equipment boxes and tool storage
- Control rooms, emergency steering
- Storage lockers and spaces
- Personal lockers
- Concealed by waste materials

continued …

Deck and external areas

- Coiled ropes
- Deck storage rooms and lockers
- Behind deck profiles and ledges
- Inside lockers and behind contents
- Battery rooms
- Switch rooms
- Chain lockers
- Lifeboats and internal storage lockers
- Cargo holds
- Bilges
- Winches and cranes
- Equipment and environmental clothing stores
- Covered cargo
- Between shipping containers and storage vessels
- Rudder area including rudder trunk, housing or compartment

Companionways

- Ducting
- Railings
- Compartments
- Behind access panels in decks, bulkheads or deckheads

Bridge, offices and control rooms

- Consoles, cupboards and lockers
- Behind instrumentation panels and boxes
- Computer arrays
- Underneath furniture

Cargo search

Many of the procedures for area search also apply to cargo search.

Searching cargo will depend on its nature and in some cases the likelihood of a security breach occurring to specific cargo items might arise. Shipping containers, loose and packaged cargo, including vehicles, can present an opportunity to hide, or conceal unauthorised items.

The search controller will have to decide the priorities for the search. Accessibility of the cargo may be one factor affecting these priorities. During a general search, all cargo areas should be checked for missing seals, broken locks and signs of being opened or forced.

In a general search the amount of cargo to be searched or examined can be reduced by establishing the likelihood of compromise. For example, loose cargo on the deck may be compromised but it is perhaps less likely that containers loaded at a CSI port could be tampered with.

Wherever possible, the cargo should be divided into logical search areas or zones and teams allocated accordingly. Concurrent actions may be useful in reducing the time to search, such as one team checking the cargo against the manifest while another physically searches the cargo.

Shipping containers are likely areas for concern. The following may give an indication that a container has been adapted for stowaways:

- Small air holes cut or drilled into the container for venting
- Lightly- or spot-welded panels and trap doors
- Strange odours and noises
- Security seals tampered with
- Inner dimensions of empty containers not matching external. False walls are often used to conceal people within a container

Containers are attractive to criminals for a host of nefarious purposes – so the search team may discover people, narcotics, weapons, contraband and any combination of these. It is important that the search team has an open mind about what its members may expect to find. If they are only searching for people, they may miss important and significant other finds.

Safety of searches

All necessary steps must be taken to ensure that search procedures are carried out with due regard for the health and safety of those conducting them. Any risk assessment tools which make up part of the vessel's SMS may be used prior to such activities.

Especially important are the requirements for working aloft and entering into confined spaces. It is likely that thorough searches may include such areas and this should be considered as part of the planning process.

Personnel detailed for search should be equipped appropriately. It is the responsibility of the search supervisor to ensure that the correct equipment is supplied.

Any necessary items should be intrinsically safe and be approved according to company requirements.

Items needed for a search

- Flashlight/torch
- Safety lamp for illumination in hazardous atmospheres
- Mirrors for inspecting underneath objects, over and on top of out-of-reach objects. Mirrors can be used with flashlights, either in conjunction with them or as an integral fitting to the mirror
- Tapes to mark searched areas or to temporarily restrict access
- Tools: screwdrivers, wrenches, bolt-croppers and crowbar
- Chemical lights to mark searched areas
- Evidence bags (plastic and paper)
- Radio or telephone
- Digital camera
- Voice recorder for witness interviews and statements
- General arrangement or deck plan, to give locations, mark search areas and for navigation of searchers around the vessel
- Notebook to record information
- Camcorder. Video content can bolster any report

Personal protective equipment suitable for the search environment and location can include hard hats, non-slip footwear, reflective vests, goggles, protective suits, gloves and masks, as appropriate. Restrictive clothing should be avoided, unless required for foul weather protection or safety. No item should be carried unless it is part of the search or safety equipment.

External searchers

Ships arriving in port are frequently boarded by various individuals with authority to search for stowaways. Often they are unaware of the dangers of entering an enclosed space or the particular hazards involved with the cargo being carried at the time. There are also dangers of crew being more engrossed in the task of searching for stowaways than the threats posed by the spaces in which they are searching. All parties engaged in searching should be made aware of the dangers.

Lessons can be learned from an unusual and tragic incident involving the death of two security service personnel conducting a ship search for stowaways.

The ship was fully laden with a cargo of coal at the time of the search. The cargo holds had not been ventilated and the Master was engaged in port arrival formalities. As part of the search operation two security personnel entered the cargo hold via an access hatch, without testing the atmosphere and without wearing breathing apparatus.

Both succumbed to the rare atmosphere and fell while descending the hold ladder. A third member of the search team attempted a rescue operation, again without proper equipment, and he also fell. The Master and ship's officers were then contacted and the hatch cover opened and a rescue operation mounted. Unfortunately, only one of the three security personnel survived.

Search training, drills and exercises

Personnel should be trained in their duties both individually and as a team. Drills and exercises are conducted to ensure that ship's personnel are conversant with the requirements of the SSP and to ensure that it can be implemented effectively. Drills and exercises will reveal any weaknesses in the SSP and also any training deficiencies and material resources.

Individual skills and techniques

- Search of cargo and ship's stores
- Search of vehicles (as applicable)
- Security equipment and systems: employment, testing, calibration and maintenance
- Individual first responder actions
- Apprehension and control of stowaways

Team skills and techniques

- Area search
- Cargo search
- Personal search
- Communications
- Cordon and evacuation
- Team first responder actions
- Questioning

Drills are normally an internal verification process, testing individual elements of the SSP or specific threat areas.

Exercises can be based on individual ships or involve external agencies such as port facilities or response organisations including law enforcement. Exercises can be 'table-top', involving key company and external personnel, or full-scale, where physical actions are carried out in response to scenarios designed to test implementation of the SSP. Validation of such exercises can be carried out by an external agency.

Exercises need to be written and managed so as to mirror reality as far as possible. Exercise aims and objectives should be clearly stated (eg to test the ship's response to loading in a port known for stowaway problems).

Exercises require a degree of planning depending on their aims and objectives and the agencies involved.

Planning an exercise

Type of exercise

- Table-top simulation
- Full-scale
- Combined with other agencies or within a larger exercise, eg port facility
- Alongside or at anchor
- Aims and objectives
- Identify the elements of the SSP that will be tested or verified. Be specific where a certain element is under scrutiny
- Identify what is expected to happen in response to the scenario and what criteria must be met in order to achieve success or compliance with the SSP
- Communication and notification procedures and the coordination of the response at all levels should all be tested

Considerations

- Scenarios written to invoke a response should be feasible and viable in reality. They should consider the training levels of the crew and the equipment available
- All applicable real-time health and safety considerations should be reviewed and incorporated into the exercise plan
- The exercise timeline should be constructed in consideration of the resources available to respond and those available to manage the exercise scenarios
- Identification of the resources required (eg participants, directing staff and materials)
- Administration. Who will coordinate the exercise and how will it be reported? As a minimum, reports should be made at the end of each exercise phase or scenario and at the end of the exercise
- The final report should include an appraisal of the exercise overall and include both positive and negative outcomes, a summary of the lessons learned and a prioritised action plan in order to rectify deficiencies
- Establish who will participate or attend and at what stage of the exercise. External agencies must be brought into the planning process as early as possible and provision made

Bomb threats

The threat of being bombed is of genuine concern to shipping today but too many SSPs contain only generic and vague guidance on the response to a bomb threat and many contain information that is potentially dangerous and misleading.

Many of these plans have been written to cover shore-based installations or cruise ships with a large array of security resources and provisions available. They call for responses and for the use of equipment and knowledge that is not realistically available on most merchant cargo vessels.

With this caveat in mind, some guidance is offered that may be applicable in most cases. This is intended as a guide and specific responses should be detailed in the vessel's SSP. If they are not adequately covered, the issue should be raised with the CSO.

The most important point to stress is the value of detailed and comprehensive preparation. A bomb incident should never catch anyone by surprise. Ensure everyone know what the SSP tells them to do. If it calls for bomb blankets and these are not available then the SSP is flawed. If the SSP states that blast route planning will be applied but no one onboard is trained in this, then even more serious problems will occur if a bomb is located.

By developing a proper ship-specific bomb incident plan and considering possible bomb incidents in the SSP, the potential for personal injury and damage to the vessel, cargo and environment can be reduced.

Bombs can be constructed to look like almost anything and can be placed or delivered in a number of ways. The only common feature is that they are designed to explode. Most bombs are homemade (improvised explosive device or IED) and are limited in their design only by the imagination of, and resources available to, the bomber.

Remember when searching for a bomb to suspect anything that looks unusual.

The majority of bomb threats are called in to the target by telephone, although occasionally these calls may be through a third party. It is less common for the threat to be communicated in writing or by a recording.

There are two logical explanations for reporting a bomb threat:

● The caller has definite knowledge, or believes, that a bomb has been, or will be, placed and wants to minimise personal injury or damage to property. The caller may be the person who placed the device or someone who has become aware of such information

● The caller wants to create panic that will result in disruption of the normal activities on the vessel or within the port facility where the device is allegedly placed

Whatever the reason for the report or threat, there is almost certain to be a reaction to it. Through proper planning, uncontrolled and dangerous reactions can be greatly reduced.

In the event of such threats, the better the preparation and readiness, the greater the chance of defeating the bomber. Through proper preparation, access to the vessel can be reduced and those areas that can be 'hardened' against the potential bomber can be identified. This will limit the amount of time lost to searching, if a search is deemed necessary.

If a bomb incident occurs, proper planning will instil confidence in the onboard security management and will reduce the possibility of panic. Once a state of panic has been reached, the potential for injury and damage is greatly increased.

Two separate but inter-dependent plans must be developed, one covering physical security and the other covering a bomb incident.

Physical security provisions protect personnel, the vessel and cargo against unauthorised entry, trespass, damage, sabotage and other illegal or criminal acts. These will be set out in the SSP and while the physical security elements may be aimed at prevention and control of access to the vessel they can obviously safeguard against an attempted bomb attack.

A bomb incident plan must provide detailed procedures to be implemented when a bomb attack is threatened or executed. It must include a definite chain of command or line of authority to give confidence and avoid panic.

Establishing a chain of command should be simple if the SSP is followed. Even if a complex situation exists, such as a threat across a whole fleet or flag, the SSO and Master of each vessel will respond to the CSO and the guidance of the relevant authorities.

In planning, a command centre should be designated. In most instances this will be the wheelhouse, although an alternative location should be identified as access to the command centre may not be possible or practical.

The vessel's security personnel assigned to operate the centre should have the authority to decide what action should be taken during the threat. Only those with assigned duties should be permitted in the centre. Provision should be made for alternatives in case someone is injured or absent when a threat is received. An updated crew list should be maintained in the command centre.

Contact the CSO and the appropriate authorities as detailed within the SSP to determine if any assistance is available in developing the physical security plan or bomb incident plan.

Training is essential to deal properly with a bomb threat incident. Instruct all personnel in what to do if a bomb threat is received. Be absolutely certain that all personnel assigned to the command centre are aware of their duties.

The positive aspects of planning will be lost if leadership is not apparent. It is also very important to organise and train an evacuation unit that will respond to the command centre that has a clear understanding of the importance of its role.

It is essential that lines of communication be established between the command centre and the search or evacuation teams. The centre must have the flexibility to keep up with the search team's progress.

Instruct all personnel, especially those likely to answer any incoming telephone calls, as to the correct response if a bomb threat call is received. If possible, it is always desirable that more than one person listens in on the call, but it is recognised that this is unlikely to be possible onboard most vessels. It should also be remembered that such calls may be placed to shipping company offices ashore, and so all personnel should be aware of the security guidance and requirements laid out in these plans.

A calm response to the caller could result in obtaining additional information. This is especially true if the caller wishes to avoid injuries or deaths. If told that the vessel cannot be evacuated in time, the caller may be willing to give more specific information on the bomb's location, components or method of initiation.

The caller is always the best source of information about the bomb.

Action when a bomb threat is called in

- Keep the caller on the line as long as possible. Ask for the message to be repeated. If possible, record every word spoken by the person or at least take detailed notes
- If the caller does not indicate the location of the bomb or the time of possible detonation, ask for this information
- Inform the caller that detonation of a bomb could result in death or serious injury to many innocent people
- Pay particular attention to background noises, such as motors running, music playing, and any other noise that may give a clue to the location of the caller
- Listen closely to the voice (male, female), voice quality (calm, excited), accents, and speech impediments. Immediately after the caller hangs up, report the threat to the SSO and Master
- Report the information immediately to the CSO, who will then inform the relevant authorities in accordance with the sequence of notification established in the SSP
- If a written threat is received, save all materials, including any envelope or container. Once the message is recognised as a bomb threat, further unnecessary handling should be avoided. Every possible effort must be made to retain evidence such as fingerprints, handwriting or typewriting/printing, paper, and postal marks. These will prove essential in tracing the threat and identifying the writer
- While written messages are usually associated with generalised threats and extortion attempts, a written warning of a specific device may occasionally be received. It should never be ignored

The most serious of all decisions to be made by the vessel's onboard management team in the event of a bomb threat is whether to:

- Ignore the threat
- Search the vessel
- Evacuate the vessel

Ignoring the threat completely can result in problems. While a statistical argument can be made that very few bomb threats are real – it is easier to threaten than to place an explosive – it cannot be overlooked that some bomb threats are indeed genuine.

Some form of response is therefore advised and necessary.

Initiating a search after a threat is received is perhaps the most sensible approach. If a device is found, then the correct response as in the SSP can be initiated.

Under no circumstances should anyone move, jerk or touch a suspicious object or anything attached to it. The removal, disarming or disposal of a bomb must be under guidance of the CSO and the relevant authorities.

Recommended procedures for suspicious objects

- Report the location and an accurate description of the object to the SSO and Master. This information should be relayed immediately to the command centre, which will notify the CSO and the relevant authorities
- Identify the danger area and block it off with a clear zone above and below the object
- Check to see that all doors and ports are open to minimise primary damage from the blast and secondary damage from fragmentation – creating a 'blast route'
- Follow the instructions of the CSO and those in the SSP
- Do not permit re-entry into, or around, the space until the device has been removed or disarmed
- No action should be taken which affects or changes the environment near the device, eg lighting, temperature, noise etc
- Do not put it in water or play water on it as this could short a control circuit and detonate it
- Do not run in the vicinity of the device
- Do not use VHF/UHF radios in the vicinity of the device
- Do not handle, touch, shake, open or move suspected explosives or suspected devices
- Do not cut, pull or touch wires, switches, fuses or fastenings
- Do not pass metallic tools near the suspected device
- Do not smoke nearby
- Do not move the device away from people; move people away from the device
- Do not direct people past the suspect device
- Do not get near bombs

Response to a bomb find

Immediate evacuation in response to a bomb threat is obviously not an alternative open to vessels at sea, although it may be when alongside.

If a device is found on board a ship in port, the Master or responsible officer should evacuate the ship in accordance with the emergency plan, retaining only sufficient staff to provide technical support to the security services.

If a device is found while a vessel is at sea, the Master's response will be based on the size and location of the device, the ship's location and the time until the security services and other assistance becomes available. Different vessel types will be under different levels of threat in the event of a potential explosion. The nature of the threat, its consequences and likelihood will have been explored as part of the security risk assessment and the decision on when and if to abandon ship.

Where practical, evacuation or abandonment should be no different from when routinely practised as part of the vessel's safety management regime. Consideration should be given to the possibility of a bomb closing off certain routes and means of escape.

The procedures, advice and routines detailed in this chapter recognise the best practices established globally by law enforcement agencies, in particular the US Bureau of Alcohol, Tobacco, Firearms and Explosives, and have been adapted for use on board merchant vessels.

In the event of an explosion

If a bomb explodes onboard or near the ship without warning or after being located, the Master should:

- Ensure water-tight integrity and stability
- Render first aid where necessary
- Take fire-fighting precautions
- Muster personnel to establish number and names of casualties
- Inform CSO, DPA, PFSO or local authorities (if in port) and make distress call (if at sea) if necessary

Do not wait to identify any weaknesses in procedures or in the SSP until it is too late. It is vital to train and carry out drills and exercises that truly recreate the likely scenarios that will develop in the event of a security breach or threat.

Chapter 9

Security equipment

KEY ADVICE

- Understanding the range of security equipment available for ships
- Assessing the most suitable equipment for particular vessels
- Understanding what is involved in the decision to employ armed guards
- Understanding the needs for training, testing, maintenance and record-keeping
- Understanding the range of security equipment available for ports

The ISPS Code imposed a small number of physical requirements in the form of mandatory security-related equipment. The amendments to SOLAS included three ship-related provisions: advancement of the date at which all ships were to be equipped with AIS, the permanent marking and display of the ship's unique identification number and the installation of a ship security alert system (SSAS).

Automatic Identification System

SOLAS Chapter V, Regulation 19, introduced the requirement for carriage of Automatic Identification System (AIS), capable of automatically communicating basic information on the ship's identity, position, heading and speed to other AIS transponders and shore-based facilities.

The introduction of AIS was discussed long before that of ISPS, with the primary aim of improving the safety of navigation, but because AIS can be used by states to monitor the movements of ships in their waters it was agreed to move forward the agreed date for implementation.

AIS acts like a transponder. Operating in the VHF maritime band, it generates in excess of 4,500 reports/minute and updates as often as every two seconds to ensure reliable ship-to-ship transmission of static and dynamic navigational data.

Position and timing information is normally received from an external GPS or DGPS receiver for precise positions in coastal and inland waters. Other information broadcast by the AIS, if available, is electronically obtained from shipboard equipment through standard data connections.

AIS is designed to operate in one of the following modes:

- Ship-to-ship for collision avoidance
- For coastal stations to obtain information about a ship and cargo
- Generation of AIS long-range data over Inmarsat-C
- As a traffic management tool when integrated with a VTS. The data generated can be displayed on the AIS or on radar or electronic chart equipment

AIS provides authorities with valuable information about routes, cargo and the ship itself, while increasing the situational awareness for those monitoring and controlling coastal and offshore waterways. There are concerns from some quarters that AIS actually compromises the security of the vessel. It is not difficult to understand these concerns. Whereas the ISPS Code imposes secrecy and restriction of information, AIS reveals the identity of a vessel and what it is doing.

From a long-term, technical perspective there is no easy fix for this. However, in reaching for the off button, many Masters who feel threatened often circumvent the argument. Official guidance on the issue of AIS and of the balance between switching it off to conceal the vessel, or keeping it on to ensure it is visible, is prone to change.

At the time of publication, recommended best practice for vessels transiting the Gulf of Aden and the Arabian Sea and at risk of attack by Somali pirates is to leave AIS transmitting across the entire High Risk Area (as defined in BMP).

AIS transmission should continue to be restricted to ship's identity, position, course, speed, navigational status and safety-related information. As noted, this is a change from the previous guidance which recommended that AIS be left on only in the Gulf of Aden. The decision on AIS policy remains at the discretion of the Master, however. If it is switched off during transit, it should be activated immediately at the time of an attack.

Ship Security Alert System

SOLAS Chapter X1-2, Regulation 6, specified that all ships of more than 500gt must be fitted with an SSAS. When an SSAS is activated, the system will transmit a ship-to-shore security alert to a competent authority designated by the flag administration. This may include the shipping company, if deemed acceptable by the flag administration.

The alarm should identify the ship and its location and indicate that the security of the ship is under threat or has been compromised. Onboard the ship, the SSAS must not raise any alarm nor send any alarm to other ships in the vicinity. The activation points are likely to be hidden from view or not readily identifiable.

Once activated the SSAS response is only audible and visible at the defined receiving station. The SSAS must be capable of being tested and senior shipboard personnel must be familiar with its operation.

Long range tracking and identification

In addition to the broadcast of vessel information in a localised area, long-range identification and tracking of ships (LRIT) was established as an international system in May 2006 by the IMO under resolution MSC.202(81), which amends SOLAS Chapter V Regulation 19-1.

LRIT allows contracting governments to request and receive position reports from vessels operating under their flag, vessels indicating their intention to enter a port under their jurisdiction or vessels operating within 1,000 nm of their coast.

The LRIT regulation applies to all passenger ships and cargo ships of 300gt and above (including high speed craft in both cases) and mobile offshore drilling units engaged in international voyages. The ship's identity and position (and the date and time of that position) must be transmitted automatically at reporting intervals from 15 minutes to six hours to the LRIT data centre designated by the flag administration.

Commonly used security equipment

The need for additional security equipment may be identified when the SSA is carried out. Where vulnerabilities are identified, security hardware can be used as an effective control to minimise the level of risk.

CSOs, SSOs and PFSOs should be aware that for all the effective and highly useful equipment supplied by respected companies there is also a trade in fakes and equipment that simply does not work. Not only is this a waste of money, it can place crews and ships in danger. Any claims made by manufacturers should be thoroughly investigated to ensure that the equipment is fit for purpose.

Access control

Locks are the simplest, cheapest and most common form of shipboard security. The most popular on board vessels are cylinder locks fitted internally (cabin doors) and padlocks used elsewhere. The most important thing to remember is that a lock is only effective if it is used properly. On many vessels padlocks hang loosely and cabins are left unlocked.

Locks will only delay determined boarders. They will not deter or stop those who have boarded the vessel for nefarious purposes, so should be used as an addition to the security regime onboard and not be overly relied upon.

Even the basic padlock is evolving and new types can be operated with electronic keys. The technology has been used in cars and 'cyber locks' are becoming increasingly sophisticated. Coded and biometric locks are opened by means of codes, swipe cards or even finger prints.

However, there is no point in purchasing such equipment if it is simply left unlocked or if information about codes is left where intruders can see it.

Some vessel operators are using barbed or razor wire to secure certain areas. This does have a potential conflict with safety and the Master, CSO and SSO should ensure that such barriers are not closing off escape routes.

Barriers and fences can be extremely effective against potential boarders but, if they are in place, it is important that this does not lead to complacency in searching and the belief that the barriers are doing the work.

Some electrified barriers are available, including the one that provides 9,000 volts of what is claimed to be non-lethal protection. These electric security systems are not suitable for all vessels, notably tankers, due to the risk of ignition.

The use of razor wire around ships has proved to be effective, yet does present hazards. It can restrict legitimate movement, which in turn can affect the safety of crew. New products are being devised all the time; one example is made up of a coil of razor wire encased in a fibre-glass canister which hangs on the outside of the ship's rail. It can be rapidly deployed, yet the crew are protected from handling dangers and will not become trapped by it.

Gates are an under-used, yet sensible, security provision. A number of vessels fit gates across the gangway entrance point, thus denying easy unauthorised access. All visitors have to wait at the gate until they are allowed to access the vessel.

The use of signs can give a strong signal and indication of the security focus onboard a vessel. Their use can be a deterrent against unauthorised access and demonstrate that security is taken seriously.

Screening equipment

People wishing to access the vessel can be screened by passing through a metal detection archway pre-set to alarm if a certain level of metal is carried through. These are similar in design to those used at airports. More common on merchant vessels is the use of hand-held metal detectors for screening individuals. However, metal detectors will not pick up explosives, plastic weapons or inflammable liquids carried in glass or plastic containers.

Metal detection should be augmented by a physical search of a percentage of those being screened, including some who do not alarm the detector. This will increase the chances of detection and act as a powerful deterrent.

Metal detectors are of little use for screening baggage and personal belongings as most bags and briefcases have locks, hinges and other metal components that would result in a very high alarm rate. Moreover, hand-held detectors have a limited depth of effective penetration.

Air sampling systems, either static or hand-held, can be used to detect high concentrations of some explosives. However, currently no commercial vapour detection system is capable of detecting all forms of explosives. X-ray equipment is an expensive option and apart from passenger ships it is very unusual to find such equipment on merchant vessels.

Modern equipment is capable of producing images of good definition and penetration. However, X-ray examination may not detect explosives and plastic weapons nor will it identify the actual liquid in bottles or other containers that are detected. Moreover, it is possible to camouflage the image of weapons and devices by the use of other dense materials, such as lead crystal glass. The use of X-ray equipment must, therefore, be accompanied by a percentage physical check of baggage, including a proportion that does not arouse suspicion.

Operator efficiency decreases significantly after only a relatively short time, so individual operators should only scan X-ray images for a maximum of 20 minutes and then be employed on other duties, such as a physical search, for 40 minutes before returning to the console. Each image should be presented for a minimum of five seconds to permit proper examination.

Any baggage whose image arouses suspicion, or contains a dark area that could conceal a weapon or device, should be physically searched.

Physical searching is the most common form of screening for people, baggage, stores and cargo. For people, this is the traditional 'pat down' which many travellers will have experienced when passing through airports.

If performed correctly, systematically and to an adequate percentage of people, bags, stores and cargo, physical searching will have a positive effect on security.

Monitoring security

Every ship should have an appropriate level of lighting, with the lights positioned to enable:

- Ship's personnel to detect activities beyond the ship, on both the shoreside and the waterside
- Illumination of the area on and around the ship
- Personnel identification at access points

Whenever the ship is alongside during port operations, such as cargo work, the ship's deck and access points to the ship should be illuminated at night and during periods of low visibility. At other times, alongside or at an offshore terminal or anchorage, illumination may be used when considered necessary. Additional lighting may be necessary to protect against the heightened risk of a security incident. When necessary, additional shoreside lighting may be arranged in coordination with the port facility.

While underway, and when considered necessary, the ship should use all the lighting available consistent with safe navigation, having regard to the current provisions of the Collision Regulations (COLREGS).

Lighting does have its limitations. Boardings can take place during daylight hours and this is the most likely time for the most common form of Somali piracy attacks. If an automated light is activated or a boarder is illuminated and spotted, then someone has to notice it and take action. Lighting on its own it is not likely to be sufficient to deter a boarder.

Shore-based establishments commonly use passive infrared sensors to trigger lighting when someone comes into its field of vision. The light can be programmed to stay on for a set time and will re-set if the cause of its activation is no longer present.

There are obvious problems with such sensors at sea, such as being triggered by the movement of legitimate personnel around the vessel. To counter this, careful consideration should be given to the positioning of such detectors. Alternatively, the lights can be manually operated.

A number of ship operators have opted for the installation of extremely high-powered searchlight units. By using these powerful lights the need for sufficient lighting alongside the vessel is solved with the installation of only two lights. The same lights can be quickly positioned to detect activities beyond the vessel, thus meeting two demands (near and distant) in one installation.

When considering the positioning of any lighting source, whether for safety or security purposes, it is always important to ensure that the lighting does not create areas of excessive shadow in which boarders can conceal themselves.

Many companies have looked to intruder detection and alarm systems to provide additional monitoring and protection of the vessel. Most AID systems rely on a combination of contacts (placed at doors, windows and portholes) and motion sensors.

The basic elements include:

- Control panel. Normally on the wheelhouse. If the alarm sounds and the security system has the capability, the control panel display will indicate which area of the vessel, or motion detector, caused the alarm
- Alarm or siren. Sounds when there has been a break-in to startle an intruder. Although this can be linked into the vessel's general alarm, this can create potential confusion in responding effectively and promptly to the boarding. A designated alarm is preferable
- Motion detectors. Passive infrared, microwave or photoelectric detectors sense changes caused by human presence. Placing needs to be carefully considered to avoid false alarms from legitimate personnel movement, as does the timing of activation
- Door, window and porthole contacts. Magnetic contacts form a circuit between a door and doorframe or a window and a frame and when the door or window is opened (and the system is on), the circuit is broken and sounds the alarm.

The installation of CCTV can help remote monitoring of means of access, spaces and other parts of the vessel. This can have a profoundly positive effect on the manpower needed to effectively monitor the security of the vessel. Fewer people are able to do more.

CCTV systems typically involve a fixed (or dedicated) communications link between cameras and monitors. This can be wireless but on most vessels the link is a fixed wire one.

Images can be recorded or beamed back to a receiver ashore if deemed necessary. There are a number of choices in recording media whether an analogue or digital recording format is used. It is considered likely that CCTV equipment on most merchant vessels (passenger ships excluded) will be used purely for monitoring purposes and that systematic recording of images will not be required.

Numerous options are available at varying costs in terms of cameras, sensors, lenses and night vision equipment. It is strongly recommended that the CSO takes specialist advice on getting the most from the CCTV system.

It should be integrated into existing security systems, including lighting. The better the light, the better the picture, especially if a light is well positioned so that it illuminates likely threats.

CCTV on ships has long been a contentious issue, particularly the monitoring of the images and positioning of equipment. If the screens are placed on the wheelhouse they could detract from watchkeeping and the safe navigation of the vessel.

Careful consideration must be given to how CCTV images will be monitored before the equipment is fitted. CCTV can be an excellent means of remotely monitoring parts of the vessel but it is only as good as the images collected and the response these trigger. If the equipment is not effectively monitored then it becomes redundant.

Security lighting can interfere with safe navigation and can lead to deterioration of the CCTV images captured. To overcome these problems it is possible to fit cameras with night vision capabilities or watchkeepers can be issued with a night vision monocular or night vision binoculars that intensify existing light.

Such equipment can be beneficial when trying to spot security threats in low light conditions but the distance at which a human-sized figure can be clearly recognised under normal conditions (moon and star light, with no haze or fog) depends on the magnifying power of the objective lens and the strength of the image intensifier.

Blast containment equipment

A number of SSPs cover the use of blast suppression or containment systems. It is the experience of the author that many vessels that state they will use such equipment do not actually have it on board. Often such guidance was written into the plan as a generic statement taken from a passenger ship SSP – which is both disturbing and potentially dangerous.

The SSO should ensure that any equipment mentioned in the plan is available on board. If it is not, the plan should either be amended or the equipment provided. It is important to note that not all crew members may completely accept the need for them to use such equipment, especially as it means being in close proximity to explosives. Training, education and drills may alleviate these very natural concerns.

A number of basic bomb containment and suppression systems are available, designed to be rapidly deployed over a suspect IED package to reduce the hazard. Bomb blast suppression bins are mobile blast containers constructed from composite woven material to withstand blast and fragments from IED devices containing up to 500g of plastic explosive.

A removable inner bag is designed to hold a suspect device in the upright position to allow X-ray inspection while in the container. The bag is fitted with handle loops to allow easy removal of the package for transportation to a safe area for further scrutiny.

The outside of the main unit is fitted with rubber tyre rings to allow the tube to be rolled away from a sensitive area without removal of the package. A detachable base plate is fitted to the unit to provide protection to the floor when in the upright position.

Bomb blast suppression blankets are used to suppress the blast fragmentation from an explosion that can cause damage and injuries. They are particularly useful for suspected IEDs contained in packages up to briefcase size and for pipe bombs.

Each blanket is used in conjunction with a ballistic collar that is placed on its edge around the suspected explosive device. The blanket is then placed over the collar and suspect device. The collar directs the force of the blast upwards into the blanket, which contains most of the fragments created by the explosion.

Two or more collars and blankets can be used to suppress larger size explosive devices. The majority of blast suppression blankets are made of multiple layer ballistic filler material that is enclosed in a heavy duty, water-resistant nylon cover fitted with lifting straps and clearly marked DANGER.

The blankets and collars fold into a compact holdall bag allowing personnel to quickly bring them to the scene of an explosive device.

Guard patrol monitoring systems

To ensure that personnel with security patrolling duties are correctly visiting all the areas assigned to them, there are a number of systems available to electronically log and monitor the patrol status.

These commonly consist of a recorder in the form of wand or baton which the guard carries. On reaching each site, the device is pressed on to the small checkpoint station and an electronic recording is made of the date, time and station number, which is then stored in the recorder's memory.

Upon returning to base, the recorder is placed in the downloader and charger. While the information is being downloaded into the computer, the battery is being charged. Some systems will also allow remote downloads of data.

In addition to providing the Master or SSO and CSO with data regarding patrols on the vessel, such systems collect evidence of effective security in the event of an audit or an expanded port state inspection. Record-keeping is an important part of the security process and such systems provide an excellent source of data.

Firearms and armed guards

There is an almost universal acceptance that the arming of seafarers is not practical or acceptable. That is not, however, the end of the armed vessel debate as the growing trend is to employ private security in high risk piracy areas and many guards are now armed.

It is increasingly common for shipowners and operators, particularly when transiting the Gulf of Aden and Indian Ocean, to look to private armed guards to protect their crew and vessels. Where there is demand there is also supply. A growing number of companies, many employing former members of elite military units, are providing teams of armed guards onto ships and armed escort vessels to support ships passing through pirate-infested waters.

This can lead to concerns over the standard of the security companies and of the personnel they are placing onboard. There is a litany of anecdotal evidence about 'bad' armed guards – from weapons accidently discharged on the wheelhouse through to accusations of gun-running. When substandard contractors are placed onboard it can be problematic and when they are armed the problems intensify.

In response to industry concerns the IMO has developed guidance on the use of privately contracted armed security personnel onboard ships in the HIGH RISK AREA. This was agreed at MSC89 (May 2011) and resulted in two sets of interim guidance – one for shipowners (MSC.1/Circ.1405) and one for flag states (MSC.1/Circ.1406).

The IMO member states have decided not to enter into the debate on whether to use armed guards or not, leaving the decision to flag states. The IMO guidelines enable shipowners and operators to confidently enter a formal due diligence process so they are satisfied that they know who they are going to employ if they decide to 'go armed'.

The moves to regulate the maritime security industry are welcome. Trade associations are one way of self-regulation. One that has evolved to help recently is the Security Association for the Maritime Industry (SAMI), an organisation whose membership is made up of private maritime security companies which are checked, verified and certified against minimum standards of conduct and procedures. All companies are being encouraged to adopt the new International Code of Conduct for Private Security Companies. Although this is primarily aimed at land-based security companies, a maritime annex is being drafted.

The IMO guidelines cover risk assessment, selection criteria, insurance cover, command and control, management and use of weapons and ammunition at all times when on board and rules for the use of force as agreed between the shipowner, the private maritime security company and the Master.

In essence, flag states can now regulate the use of armed security service providers and hold them accountable for their actions. The approval of such security companies and their personnel, including any licensing or certification, will be a flag state responsibility after appropriate vetting and background checks. Indeed, flag states must decide not only whether employment is appropriate and lawful on their vessels but whether each of the privately contracted armed security guards meets the minimum criteria as laid down in the guidelines. The issue has been passed externally from the IMO to the International Organization for Standardization (ISO). ISO 28007 includes Procedures for Private Maritime Security Companies.

Another area of interest and concern is the status of these armed security guards while onboard. Are they part of the ship's crew or are they supernumeraries? This is very complex and the ramifications, especially in light of the soon to be ratified International Labour Organisation's MLC are significant. After much discussion, it has been agreed that this was a matter for each individual flag state to decide.

The twin issues of legal implications and potential liability have naturally been a concern. Discussions on the issue of the Master's responsibility and liability were extensive and there are concerns where the actions of one of these armed security personnel may cause injury or death to any person, including the guards themselves, or any other damage caused to the ship or its cargo.

Different opinions were voiced as to what extent the Master could be held liable in such cases. There was concern over the possible legal consequences a Master could face and the fact that Masters are deemed to have overriding authority could be construed in such a way that they can be held ultimately responsible for any actions taken by the privately contracted armed security personnel which were actually beyond their control.

This is a very real and live issue and the guidelines take a view from the perspective of the command and control structure. It is important that any contracts contain a clear statement that at all times the Master remains in command and retains the overriding authority on board. The IMO noted the distinction between uses of the terms 'authority' and 'responsibility', and it is hoped this will protect all parties when there is any future apportionment of liability.

What do the IMO guidelines say?

At their most basic level, the IMO guidelines require that a risk assessment should be carried out. There has to be a formal risk assessment underpinning the decision to employ armed guards. The assessment should include and document the following factors and considerations:

- Vessel and crew security, safety and protection
- Whether all practical means of self-protection have been effectively implemented in advance
- Potential misuse of firearms resulting in bodily injury or death
- Potential for unforeseen accidents
- Liability issues
- Potential for escalation of events
- Compliance with international and national law

Due diligence before selecting a private military security company includes investigation and enquiries in relation to:

- Company structure and place of registration
- Company ownership
- Financial position (annual accounts, bank references)
- Extent of insurance cover (in particular covering third party risks)
- Senior management experience
- Quality management indicators (eg ISO accreditation)

The private military security company should be able to provide documentary evidence, which may include:

- Maritime (as opposed to land-based) experience
- Authority, change in command, responsibilities in lifesaving
- Understanding of the requirements of flag, port and coastal states with respect to carriage and usage of firearms
- Availability of written testimonials and references from previous clients in the maritime industry
- Availability of documentary evidence that firearms are procured, transported, embarked and disembarked legally
- Understanding of the Somalia-based piracy threat, including the military operations in the area, and the means to maintain current knowledge
- Understanding of BMP and, in particular, ship protection measures
- Access to legal advice (eg in-house counsel or external legal advisers) on a 24/7 basis

As the quality of the service delivery depends to a great extent on the quality and experience of the individuals that make up the onboard armed guards, selection and vetting of that team is essential. The security company should demonstrate that it has verifiable, written internal policies and procedures for determining suitability of employees.

The private security company should be able to provide documentary evidence, which may include:

- Criminal background checks
- History of employment checks
- Military and law enforcement background checks, where applicable
- Records of medical, physical, and mental fitness of personnel (including drug and alcohol testing)
- Verifiable system in place to ensure continued suitability for employment of personnel
- Documentary evidence of relevant experience and certification in the use and carriage of firearms to be deployed
- Systems for provision of security identity documentation, travel documents and visas

The shipowner should verify that the private security company has adequate training procedures in place. Records of that training should give confidence that the security guards have been provided with appropriate knowledge and skills. The guidelines do not specify what 'adequate' training is and this could be a potential stumbling block for any companies looking to circumvent the guidance.

The security company should be able to provide documentary evidence, which may include:

- Comprehensive and detailed records of training, both initial and refresher, available for inspection
- Subject to any additional requirements of the flag state, security guards have received, as a minimum, shipboard familiarisation training
- Personnel trained and qualified to documented company standards in the appropriate use of force following recognised principles and guidelines recognised by the flag state
- Personnel trained to operate the specific firearms and other security equipment that will be used on the vessels on which they will be deployed
- Personnel given medical training to a recognised international standard
- Personnel given appropriate training and briefing with specific reference to the vessel type, where that vessel will be trading, and the provisions of the ISPS Code, ISM Code and BMP

Owners and operators should verify that the security company maintains insurance cover for itself, its personnel and third-party liability cover and that the its terms of engagement do not prejudice or potentially prejudice the shipowners' cover.

Liabilities, losses and expenses arising out of the deployment of armed security guards may impact on the shipowner's property and liability insurance cover. The IMO reminds owners and operators to consult with their insurers before contracting with and embarking the guards to assess the potential impact on their insurance cover, particularly as it relates to armed engagements and liability insurance held by the security company.

Security companies should provide evidence that they hold and will maintain for the duration of the contract:

- Public and employers' liability insurance cover to an appropriate level and as required by the shipowner
- Personal accident, medical expenses, hospitalisation and repatriation insurance for personnel

The security company should insure its personnel to carry and use firearms on the high seas and territorial waters, for accident, injury and damage arising from the use of firearms and liability for any claim that might arise from the carriage and the use of firearms.

It is vital that owners and operators, charterers and underwriters review all provisions in their charters and policies and ensure adequate attention is paid to the questions raised.

Armed security guards – team size, composition and equipment

Minimum secure manning is an interesting point – just how many armed security guards are needed onboard? Some at the IMO felt a risk assessment could define a quantitative level, but this argument has its flaws. For instance, if pirates employ swarming tactics a security team would be swamped, and an incorrect risk assessment would not have alerted the company to this potential outcome.

BIMCO suggested that a minimum of four armed guards should be placed on each vessel. This quantifiable recommendation should prevent understaffing. The size, composition and equipment of the proposed armed secuity team should be carefully discussed and agreed as necessary by the shipowner contracting with the security company.

Factors for consideration may include:

- Size of the armed security team. This will be influenced by factors including estimated time of the vessel transit and latest threat assessment
- Agreed duties of the armed security team – will they act as additional lookouts, assist with rigging self-protection measures? The size and type of vessel is influential
- Ship safety certificate. The size of the armed security team plus the crew should not exceed that specified in the ship's safety certificate. If the ship safety certificate requirements cannot be met due to added security personnel the flag administration should be consulted.
- Composition. It is important that there is an appropriate hierarchy, experience and skill mix within the onboard armed security team. The team leader should be competent in vessel vulnerability and risk assessments and be able to advise on ship protection measures. It is recommended that one of the armed personnel be qualified as the team medic
- Equipment requirements. This will be influenced by factors including estimated time of the vessel transit, latest threat assessment, agreed duties of the armed security team and the size and type of vessel. Enhanced medical equipment is recommended

Command and control of the onboard security team

An owner or operator entering into a contract with a security company should ensure that the command and control structure linking the ship operator, Master, ship's officers and the armed security team leader has been clearly defined and documented.

Further, before boarding the armed guards, the shipowner should ensure that the Master and crew are briefed and exercises are planned and conducted so that all roles and responsibilities are understood by all personnel on board before to entering the high risk area. In order to provide the required clarity, the documented command and control structure should include:

- A clear statement that at all times the Master remains in command, and retains the overriding authority on board
- A clearly documented set of vessel and voyage specific governance procedures, including procedures for conducting exercises based on these procedures

- A documented list of duties, expected conduct, behaviour and documentation of armed security guards' actions on board
- Transparent two-way information flow and recognisable coordination and cooperation between the shipowner, the charterer, the armed guards, the security company and the vessel's master, officers and crew

Factors to determine whether the structure is working may include:

- Provision of regular updated intelligence-based threat assessments throughout the contracted period on board and use of this information for proposed vessel routeing and amending if required to suit the ships contractual arrangements
- Monitoring daily activities of the onboard security team
- The need for a 24-hour emergency response and contingency plan to cover all potential actions
- Feedback on crew training and ship-hardening requirements based upon reports received from the security guards

Management of firearms and ammunition

An essential requirement of the security guards team will be to demonstrate responsible management and use of weapons and ammunition at all times when on board. Issues to be considered should include:

- Documented compliance with the relevant flag, coastal and port state legislation
- Verification against inventory of the transport and provision of firearms, ammunition and security equipment Appropriate containers for firearms, ammunition and security equipment at the point of transfer to the ship
- Documented standards and procedures for a complete inventory of all firearms, ammunition and security equipment available aboard the vessel upon arrival. The inventory should detail make, model, calibre and serial number of all firearms and details and quantity of ammunition
- Control procedures for separate and secure onboard stowage and deployment of firearms, ammunition and security equipment
- Confirmation of areas where firearms may or may not be carried, together with the weapon state (eg unloaded and magazine off, magazine on and safety catch on and no round chambered) and what initiates any change
- Detailed and exercised orders for when firearms can be loaded and made ready for use should be confirmed, trained and documented during certain periods as listed in the security guard contract, to ensure the highest of safety and operational capabilities for use of arms aboard the vessel
- Inventory of all arms and ammunition from the vessel reconciled on disembarkation

Rules for the use of force

It is essential that all armed security guards have a complete understanding of the rules for the use of force (RUF), as agreed between shipowner, the security company and Master, and fully comply with them. The primary function of the armed team to prevent boarding, using the minimal force necessary. Some companies suffer from a reputation for 'gung ho' responses but this has no place in these operations. The security company should provide a detailed graduated response plan to pirate attacks as part of its team's operational procedures.

The security company should require its personnel to take all reasonable steps to avoid the use of force. If force is deemed necessary and then used, it should be in a manner consistent with applicable law. In no case should the use of force exceed what is strictly necessary and it should be proportionate to the threat and appropriate to the situation.

Private security companies should require that their personnel only use firearms against persons in self-defence, to defend others against the imminent threat of death or serious injury, or to prevent the perpetration of a serious crime involving grave threat to life. This is a key tenet of the IMO guidelines and of the reluctant acceptance by its members of the need for armed guards on merchant vessels.

Reporting and record-keeping

Record-keeping is a very important aspect of the use of armed guards. The Master should maintain a log of every circumstance in which firearms are discharged, whether accidental or deliberate. Such actions should be fully documented in sufficient detail and held as a formal written record of the incident.

The requirements of a formal written report of an incident should include:

- Time and location
- Details of events leading up to the incident
- Written statements by all witnesses and those involved from the vessel crew and security team
- Identity and details of personnel involved
- Details of the incident
- Injuries or material damage sustained
- Lessons learned and, where applicable, recommended procedures to prevent a recurrence

In the event that the security guards use force, their team leaders should be advised to photograph or video (if appropriate) people and locations and log, report and collate contemporaneous written statements from all persons present at the incident in anticipation of legal proceedings.

In addition to incident reporting it is suggested that following a tour of duty the PCASP team should submit a full report to the shipowner or ship operator, via their employers if required, giving full details of the deployment, operational matters and any training or ship-hardening conducted, and offering advice as to any further enhancements to security that may be considered.

Shipowners and ship operators should ensure that the Master and the crew are made familiar with the guidelines. A key to the safe use of armed teams onboard is through engagement with the Master and crew. Where Masters are engaged and involved in the risk assessment and can see the reasons why a team should be used, or perhaps not used, this improves relationships onboard and enhances security.

Recommendations for flag states

Flag states have very different pressures to contend with and ultimately they have to determine whether the use of armed guards is appropriate and lawful. MSC.1/Circ.1406 encourages flag states to check that their owners have undertaken the due diligence required under MSC.1/Circ. 1405.

They will have to determine if, and under which conditions, this will be authorised and should take into account the possible escalation of violence that could result from the use of firearms and carriage of armed personnel on board ships.

As a first step, consideration should be given as to whether the use of armed guards would be permitted under domestic law and would be an appropriate measure to augment security arrangements under some circumstances.

As a second step, if the use of armed guards is determined to be an appropriate and lawful measure, policies should be established may include:

- Minimum criteria or requirements for private company armed security personnel, taking into account the guidance to shipowners, ship operators, and Masters
- Processes for authorising the use of private company armed security personnel who meet minimum requirements
- Processes to authorise shipowners, ship operators or shipping companies to use private company armed security personnel
- Terms and conditions under which the authorisation is granted and the accountability for compliance associated with that authorisation
- References to any flag state laws covering the carriage and use of firearms by private company armed security personnel and their relationship with the Master while onboard
- Reporting and record-keeping requirements

In addition, flag states have to provide information to the IMO on the levels of usage of private company armed security personnel onboard their vessels for circulation to member states. This will hopefully provide very important feedback to the shipping industry on the true levels of armed security. Given previous efforts to get flag state feedback, this may not paint the whole picture.

Licensing of weapons

There are still problems and issues relating to the weapons used. Stephen Askins of Ince & Co has written on the subject of weapon licensing regimes. He says that many countries impose complex requirements. In fact, UK Export Controls extend to cover UK companies and nationals (wherever they are) and even to foreign companies set up by UK nationals, where the foreign company is set up and through the course of business transfers weapons between third party countries.

What is certain is that it is a legal minefield through which private security companies must navigate and, given high profile failures such as the seizure of weapons and foreign security guards in Eritrea, it is clear that problems exist. Many security companies may simply be ignoring these regulations – sometimes through ignorance and sometimes to gain competitive advantage.

As the shipping industry becomes more reliant on armed guards, it is clear that the development and streamlining of weapon licensing laggs behind. There are many complex issues, such as the use of floating armouries, which serve to further complicate the issue.

Technological developments

Long range acoustic device

Long range acoustic devices came to prominence when one was used to keep at bay pirates who were attacking the cruise ship *Seabourn Spirit* off Somalia in 2005. Since then, reports indicate the device's limited effectiveness in the field, as pirates adapted their tactics to compensate for its use and even used ear defenders in some cases.

Negative feedback from vessels that have used the device stress the size and weight of the equipment. In many cases it can take several people to move it and this potentially places them in harm's way. Equally, when pirates swarm vessels, it can be impractical to target all the attackers.

Laser devices

High-powered lasers have been used to incapacitate pirates by dazzling them as they approach. One non-lethal weapon is effective against moving targets more than 1.5 km away. The device effectively hides the vessel carrying it in a bright green glare from the laser, forcing the pirates off course and leaving them unable to aim their weapons accurately.

It reportedly works in daylight as well as at night and is being developed so that it can be used with high-frequency surface radar that can pick up the kind of small, fast vessels used by Somali pirates. The system then automatically directs the laser towards the target. It can also rapidly fire beams at multiple targets to produce an intense flickering effect that increases the dazzle.

The laser uses powers within the safety limits that do not cause blindness in case the system mistakes an innocent vessel as a threat. The system will have to be approved for use under the UN's protocol on blinding laser weapons before it can be deployed.

Broadband radars

Traditional marine radars are notoriously poor at picking up fast and small targets, thus putting merchant vessels at a disadvantage. If watchkeepers were able to spot an incoming launch or skiff at long enough range, then the defenders would gain the advantage and an appropriate security response could be initiated. Failure to spot the threat is a real problem.

Broadband (high-frequency surface) radar enables watchkeepers to monitor important targets at ranges down to 1/32 nm and they can also expect 2-3 metres target resolution to 15 km with a maximum range of 24 nm.

The systems integrate both long-range conventional (pulse) radar and short-range broadband radar. Usual navigation radars suffer from blind spots, where the signals are obscured by masts and funnels and in particular the astern view.

The ability to spot small, fast-moving targets can be vital in gaining time when attacked by pirates, so the benefits of the next generation radars could be significant.

Propeller arrestors

Propeller arrestors form a physical barrier of 100 metres lines of buoyant polypropylene rope streamed down the sides and from the stern of the vessel to create an impenetrable security perimeter. Any attempt by a small vessel (such as a pirate skiff) to cross the rope lines will result in its propeller getting entangled and cause the engine to stop, ultimately thwarting the hijack.

They are deployed on 10 metre booms either side of the hull, from the bow to the stern, running aft the full length of the vessel. Units are also placed around the stern creating a 'no go' zone around the vessel. It is claimed that the ropes pose no threat to the host vessel's propeller.

The system is designed to remain deployed for the duration of transit through the danger zone. A range of similar systems is available and while demonstrations of some have been inconclusive others have been successfully launched.

Glass protection

Somali pirates often fire repeatedly at the wheelhouse of the vessel they are attacking in the hope of forcing the Master to slow down or stop. While vessel superstructures are remarkably robust, all too often the windows and port holes are not and if shots cause them to shatter this has safety and psychological implications.

A range of solutions for window protection exist, from permanent removal of existing glass and replacement with bullet-proof panes to temporary solutions that fit over the existing glass and can be demounted after use. Options for wheelhouse windows and accommodation ports also include gratings and films to provide protection against shattered glass caused by rocket-propelled grenades.

Water cannon

An early solution to the problem of pirates and boarders was the use of basic ship fire hoses. However, their use puts the crew operating them in harm's way as an easy target. As high-powered water is a good deterrent, the use of remotely-operated water hose units has emerged as a solution. With vision feeds and a joystick, operators can pick off individual boarders and aim the water stream directly out to sea to flood and sink pirate skiffs.

Water cannons come in a variety of sizes and weights and there are sophisticated systems designed for integration with infrared and CCTV cameras, as well as early detection radar systems. The cannons can hit a moving target over 90 metres away and hit it hard. The most powerful systems can shoot out water at a rate of 5,000 litres a minute.

There are also rotating cannon systems which, once activated, throw out a high-speed water fence that surrounds the ship's perimeter and makes it virtually impossible for anyone to board.

Pepper spray

Pepper spray is used in the one system, which consists of a 300 gallon pressurised tank connected to piping installed around the vessel to create a 30 metre defensive zone extending outwards. When activated, it disperses a high volume shower of pepper spray, which causes intense pain and short-term loss of vision.

Air cannon

Another system utilises a small air cannon that uses compressed air to fire projectiles hundreds of yards across the sea. Ships can fire a shell packed with golf balls which will travel up to 550 metres at up to 450mph and is capable of bombarding attacking pirate skiffs.

Security equipment objectives

The security equipment industry is evolving rapidly and the guidance contained here cannot cover every piece of equipment that may be encountered on a vessel or purchased to increase its security.

CSOs should be aware of the equipment options available to improve the security of the vessels for which they are responsible. It is also vital that SSOs are familiar with the equipment onboard and request training and guidance if necessary. If security is reliant on a piece of equipment as stated within the SSP, then that equipment must be in place, operational and correctly maintained.

Inspections

If, following an initial survey or examination, a contracting government inspector has clear grounds for believing that the ship does not correspond substantially with the requirements of SOLAS and the ISPS Code, or that the Master or crew are not familiar with essential shipboard security procedures, a more detailed inspection may be carried out.

Inspectors will assess whether there is any security equipment installed aboard the vessel and if it is functioning properly.

It is important that the SSO is aware of all security-related devices and equipment. A checklist, such as detailed below, can assist in ensuring that all equipment is accounted for, that its operation is understood and that it can be tested and maintained according to the manufacturer's guidelines.

Equipment checklist

- What security equipment is onboard?
- How it is operated?
- What it is used for?
- Who is responsible for each piece of equipment?

Testing

- What needs to be tested?
- What is the best way to test?
- When should this be done?
- How often?
- In what circumstances?
- Awareness of manufacturer instructions?
- Is the equipment covered within a vessel's planned maintenance system?
- What must be taken into consideration?

Maintenance and calibration

- Who is responsible?
- What extent?
- How often?

Records must be kept of all maintenance, calibration and testing of any security equipment provided on board, including the testing of the SSAS.

Security equipment and system limitations

There should be a documented training regime in place for security equipment to ensure that shipboard personnel are fully conversant with its operation. This should replicate the systems in place for training within the SMS.

The marine environment is a tough one for equipment and often security equipment not designed for the maritime industry is used on board ship. In some instances this has failed and led to worrying gaps in the vessel's ability to provide the security screening and monitoring capabilities as laid down in the SSP and required by the ISPS Code.

Security equipment may be different from that previously used by ship personnel. It is important that it is set up correctly and calibrated in accordance with the manufacturer's instructions and with the vessel's planned maintenance system schedule.

Testing of equipment is a key part of ensuring the continued effectiveness of security. Port state inspectors may ask questions on the testing and operation of key security equipment and it is imperative that all personnel with responsibilities for such items are familiar with the processes and procedures.

Training in the maintenance and repair of security equipment is important. If equipment cannot be maintained or repaired so as to ensure its continued effectiveness then this information should be relayed between the Master or SSO and the CSO. If necessary, a decision should be made to amend the SSP and provide alternative arrangements for onboard security.

Security equipment is only as good as the response it produces and it is vital that vigilance is demonstrated in monitoring equipment. Alarms that go unanswered or CCTV images that are ignored waste resources and damage the effectiveness of the security regime.

Vigilance is vital and the security equipment is only a part of the integrated security approach that must be demonstrated on vessels.

Ports and port facilities

Many ports are fitted with a mix of sophisticated and traditional security equipment. Investment within some of the world's major ports has been immense and has seen the latest technology employed to secure the port facilities and the whole port infrastructure.

Fencing

Perimeter fencing is one of the most obvious and visible forms of port protection. The perimeter of any port represents the first layer of security and is a defined mark between the port and other land, either private or public.

As the perimeter is the first opportunity for a security system to be installed it also gives the most time to react effectively to any attempted intrusions. It should also guard against unsuspecting members of the public wandering in to an area where their safety may be put at risk.

Fencing should be of suitable height, materials and construction to safeguard against the perceived risk but not impede detection of threats. Some perimeter protection measures do not stop at simple fencing. Ports use 9,000-volt shock wires, which can be installed on existing fences. Some vessels are now installing similar electric fences around vessels.

Intruder detection sensors

In addition to fencing, sophisticated outdoor security sensors can be installed around the perimeter to detect intruders as soon as they enter a protected area and before they can gain access to vessels, people or cargo. Detection is by vibration, heat, sound or movement.

The most appropriate sensor to use depends on:

- Perceived threat and level of protection required
- Effectiveness of the sensor against the threat
- Site conditions and environment
- Sensor cost comparisons
- Life cycle or cost of ownership of the sensor

PFSOs must remember that these outdoor sensors operate in a more challenging arena than those used in indoor security. Environmental conditions, such as temperature extremes, rain, snow, animals, blowing debris, seismic effects, terrain and traffic, must all be taken into account.

When functioning under these adverse conditions, the system must continue to maintain a high probability of detection while minimising false alarms (alarms with unknown causes) and nuisance alarms (environment-related alarms).

Volumetric sensors generate an invisible detection field that locates moving intruders. As the field of detection is invisible, the sensors are very difficult to evade. Immune to most environmental conditions, these sensors are often used in sterile zones and may be totally covert.

Fence and wall-mounted sensors are triggered when an intruder disturbs the detection field or when vibration due to cutting or climbing on a metal fabric fence causes an alarm. Barrier sensors are a two-in-one security option, as they provide a barrier to intrusion and a sensor system for detection.

Taut-wire sensors are an example that offers an almost zero false alarm rate and unsurpassed probability of detection. These sensors have virtually no environmental limitations and are able to provide reliable service for many years.

CCTV systems

A video motion detection system transforms the assessment-only ability of CCTV cameras by analysing the video output signal to create the detection field. Video motion detection also provides additional information to help identify the source of an alarm and whether or not it is valid. CCTV cameras are an important element in outdoor security as they can be used to verify whether alarms reported by intrusion detection sensors are valid or false or nuisance alarms, ensuring that only valid alarms are responded to.

CCTV assessment is especially important for large ports with limited security response provisions, making response to nuisance alarms particularly costly. Ports often install CCTV systems that are far more technologically advanced than on ships and many are linked to other security systems as part of an integrated approach.

Often the CCTV footage is recorded remotely at a secure location where it may easily be accessed should the primary system be compromised. The recorded images can be viewed from any PC with internet access from anywhere in the world. Live images can be viewed remotely from anywhere on a PC or even a GSM mobile phone.

Number plate recognition

Many ports, particularly larger ones within the CSI initiative, have installed number plate recognition systems to record and log the vehicles that come into the port. Automatic identification of car number plates is of great benefit for a wide variety of applications other than security and crime detection, such as the planning of cargo movements.

These systems are expensive and sophisticated. They consist of a camera, processor and an end-user application (such as access control and a database of vehicles). Placement is important. There have been extremely expensive systems positioned in such a way that inward traffic has blocked the view of outward, and *vice versa*. It is important that the system has clear views of movement in order to function effectively.

Security Lighting

There are three basic security lighting systems: dusk-to-dawn, motion-activated and hi-lo motion-activated.

Dusk-to-dawn is the oldest technique and is based on the theory that a brightly lit area discourages a would-be intruder. It requires the use of dusk-to-dawn photocell controls or lights with built-in photocells.

The downside is that lights are burning all night every night. Costs of energy and lamp replacement can be very high. In addition, it can be argued that a constantly lit area gives no indication of a security breach.

Motion-activated lighting is triggered by an intruder approaching the port or a secure area. It has become extremely popular as a security measure on account of its convenience and low cost. Lights only go on when needed, saving energy most of the night, and lamps last much longer.

The hi-lo form of lighting combines the benefits of both systems. The lights turn on at approximately 20% of their lamp wattage from dusk-to-dawn but will brighten to full brilliance when their sensors detect movement.

Cargo screening

Screening of cargo is a vital part of any port security regime but must be considered against the requirements of commerce and the need to keep cargo moving as quickly as possible. A number of technologies are employed, using different methods of scanning objects for the presence of drugs, weapons and explosives.

Detection methods include x-ray, backscatter x-ray, gamma ray and fast (or high-energy) neutron scans. They vary in size and configuration, including small hand-held devices, stationary devices (as used in airports for baggage scan) and large fixtures for container or truck scanning. Two of the tradeoffs, however, are their high cost and slow speed.

Port facilities are vulnerable to attacks from underwater divers and remotely operated underwater vehicles (ROVs). The challenge is to protect the port infrastructure by identifying counter-technologies to combat possible attacks without adversely impacting the port's capability to trade.

Underwater detection and monitoring

In many ports the risk of attack is countered by the same means, using specially trained divers and ROVs as a proven method for underwater surveillance and inspection of ships and docking areas. ROVs vary in size and configuration, number and type of cameras, mechanical tools, presence of sonar and other sensors. There are a number of commercially available ROVs specifically designed for harbour security.

An alternative approach is the use of stationary underwater installations equipped with sonar and other acoustic technologies. A number of systems are available that are capable of detecting divers approaching ships or waterside facilities.

Sonar is used to detect anything large enough to be a threat, up to a range of 800 metres. During tests, it was able to detect an approaching underwater scuba swimmer at 900 metres. There are some underwater weapons available that can disable approaching divers and swimmers. One uses sound waves tuned to cause severe gastric distress in humans. When activated the system causes the attacker to vomit.

Physical barriers

Waterside barriers have been developed to block waterborne access to harbours, docks or vessels. These are in the form of booms, similar to those used to protect installations from marine pollution. Some of the more successful systems take the form of modular marine floating breakwaters. These were initially designed for beach erosion control and have been harnessed for use against small craft seeking to break into restricted waterside areas.

While such systems are acceptable for use against smaller vessels, the challenge for future barriers is the capability to stop larger ocean-going ships.

Boat patrols

Although boat patrols may be expensive and labour-intensive, they have a role in many ports to deter criminals, pirates, stowaways and terrorists.

US ports often use dedicated Homeland Security personnel in armed response vessels to provide a very visible indication of the emphasis placed on security. This is also done in other countries, particularly around high-risk installations such as terminals for passengers, oil, LNG and LPG.

Adequate control and identification of such patrol vessels is vital, as it may become possible for criminals to disguise their intentions and presence alongside legitimate patrol vessels.

Vessel traffic services

The provision and use of vessel traffic services (VTS) can have a very positive effect on the security of a port, river or chokepoint. VTS officers have long provided safety and navigational advice to mariners and their role often encompasses security. VTS provides a strong system of vessel monitoring, enabling identification of unusual vessel movements. It also controls the movement of vessels and some VTS equipment records both the radar images and any VHF interactions – which may be important in the event of a breach of security.

In Europe, EU rules have been introduced to set up a vessel traffic monitoring and information system in which all member states will be interconnected by SafeSeaNet. The measures aim to increase maritime safety and ensure that member states are better equipped to assist ships in distress. There are inevitably security implications.

However, the measures have not been uniformly enacted into national legislation and the European Maritime Safety Agency (EMSA) is working to persaude a number of governments trying to force adoption.

Chapter 10
Making security work

The exact details of the security regime decided upon are dependent on the type of vessel and company and the areas in which they operate. However, the basic requirements and guidance are contained within the ISPS Code which lays down a clear framework to manage security, for which companies and personnel have responsibilities and duties.

At its most basic level the maritime security regime onboard ship will need seafarers to escort visitors, search people and baggage, patrolling the vessel and keeping a thorough and permanent gangway watch.

However, there is much more to security than such simple steps and with a range of very real threats to shipping and ports to consider it is vital that security is properly and effectively embraced as a part of everyday operations.

It is imperative that all think about such security duties and the way they impact on people, vessels, ports and cargoes. All individuals should understand that they are a vital link in the security chain and their actions can and do make a difference to the security of maritime transport.

Compliance with maritime security legislation is not enough to ensure that the maritime supply chain is secure. It takes more, and all involved must constantly consider the security of their domain and must be knowledgeable and feel confident to act to ensure continued security.

So how can we ensure the security regime, procedures and measures work? The first rule is to **ACCEPT** security. This acronym can be a useful reminder of some of the key elements of providing proper and effective security within a ship, port or company.

Apply risk management

The knowledge required to identify and respond to threats is gained through the application of adequate risk management intelligence.

It is imperative that the CSO, SSO and PFSO continually assess security threats and vulnerabilities and apply similar risk management techniques and skills to that embraced by the shipping industry with regard to safety.

Contemporary security knowledge

Security knowledge has to be kept up-to-date. In the same way that navigational charts that are thought to be corrected are more dangerous than ones that are known to be out-of-date, threat awareness must be corrected and updated.

Flag states should keep the CSO informed of any security information. This in turn should be given to the SSO to implement properly onboard the vessel.

Create a security culture

Outside of the piracy High Risk Area, there has been a degree of antipathy from seafarers about security and a fear of the added burden that the ISPS Code has brought with it. All personnel must be involved in the processes and understand the benefits for themselves.

The ship is a seafarer's home and needs to be protected as such. All have a role to play and a right to live and work within a secure environment. Compliance is not the end of the process, rather the beginning.

Enhance policies and procedures

The lessons learned in implementing the ISM Code are applied to ISPS operational security policies and procedures have been developed on board.

Only by enhancing the policies and procedures will the steps become effective. Rules have to be in place to make a vessel secure and these have to apply directly to the vessel, the hazards faced and take due regard to the resources available to deal with them. It is the responsibility of the company to ensure that rules are in place and that they work to allow a vessel to comply with the Code to make it more secure.

Protective measures

In consideration of the potential security hazards facing a vessel, the SSA will have identified certain protective measures or safeguards.

These safeguards are recommended to lower the risk to an acceptable level but any proposed measures require careful planning and introduction. They have to be effective and all seafarers have a vital role in making sure these safeguards work. The safeguards may be increased patrols, escorts or guarding of restricted areas – if so, shipboard personnel are the vital link in securing their vessel.

Training commitment

For personnel to implement the provisions of the ISPS Code and to make them work requires knowledge and confidence. This only comes through training, so it is vital to embrace a commitment to education and continuous improvement.

Companies need to provide personnel with the skills to perform a security role, whether by external training or shipboard drills. It is vital that all begin to understand and appreciate security, the ways that security changes working habits and patterns, and also the role that each individual has in keeping the vessel secure.

Much investment and attention has been given by nation states to the control and security of land borders. However, the need to police maritime security is even more pressing.

The sea is an open space and the threats that can arrive through maritime transport and trade are many and varied.

To protect against terrorism, control the flow of narcotics and contraband and ensure that migration is controlled – all these require a robust and effective security regime. Add to this the potential trade implications of actions by pirates and terrorists against vessels carrying vital fuel, food and raw materials and it is clear that maritime security is crucial in safeguarding many aspects of modern life.

Abbreviations

AID Automated intruder detection

CBP Customs and Border Protection (USA)

CSI Container Security Initiative

CSO Company security officer

DoS Declaration of Security

IED Improvised explosive device

ILO International Labour Organization

IMO The International Maritime Organization

IPE Individual protective equipment

ISM Code International Management Code for the Safe Operation of Ships and for Pollution Prevention

ISM SMC Safety Management Certificate

ISPS Code The International Ship and Port Facility Security Code

ISSC International Ship Security Certificate

MARPOL Convention on the Prevention of Maritime Pollution

MLC Maritime Labour Convention 2006

MTSA Maritime Transportation Security Act

NOA Notice of Arrival

NOR Notice of Readiness

PCASP Privately contracted armed security personnel

PFSO Port Facility Security Officer

PSC Port State Control

PSI Proliferation security initiative

ROVs Remotely operated underwater vehicles

RSO Recognised Security Organisation

RUF Rules for the use of force

SID Seafarer's Identity Document

SOLAS Convention Safety of Life at Sea

SSA Ship Security Assessment

SSAS Ship Security Alert System

SSO Ship Security Officer

SSP Ship security plan

STCW Convention Standards of Training, Certification and Watchkeeping

TWIC Transportation Worker Identification Credential

TSA Transportation Security Administration (of the USA)

USCG US Coast Guard

About the Author

Steven Jones MSc BSc (Hons) MNI

Steven Jones MSc BSc (Hons) MNI is Maritime Director of SAMI, the Security Association for the Maritime Industry. He spent a decade working as a navigation officer in the merchant navy and was attacked by pirates while serving. After moving ashore he advised numerous shipping companies on security planning – spending years researching, applying and developing an in-depth knowledge of security and the International Ship and Port Facility Security (ISPS) Code.

This knowledge has provided the basis for this publication and the accompanying maritime security suite of handbooks. He has also contributed articles to The Nautical Institute's magazine Seaways and other publications.

His primary focus is on the human element – particularly the ways and means of bringing security techniques and effective management to the attention of crews of merchant vessels, office personnel and ship operators. He has experience across the maritime industry, working for shipping companies, insurers, publishers and professional bodies. As well as SAMI he is the founder of the International Dynamic Positioning Operators Association (IDPOA). He is a Member of The Nautical Institute, the Chartered Institute of Public Relations and a Fellow of the Royal Society of Arts.

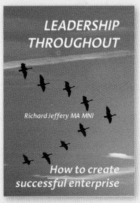